WHAT'S HOT ON THE MOON TONIGHT?

The Ultimate Guide to Lunar Observing

Andrew Planck

MoonScape Publishing, LLC

What's Hot on the Moon Tonight: The Ultimate Guide to Lunar Observing
Copyright © 2015 Andrew Planck

Books may be purchased by contacting the publisher or author through the website below:
AndrewPlanck.com

Cover and Interior Design: Nick Zelinger (NZ Graphics)
Publisher: MoonScape Publishing, LLC
Editor: John Maling (Editing By John)
Manuscript Consultant: Judith Briles (The Book Shepherd)

ISBN: 978-0-9908769-0-8
Library of Congress Catalog Number: 2014918951

1) Science   2) Astronomy   3) Moon

First Edition Printed in USA

Dedicated to my wife, Susan,
and to my two daughters, Sarah and Stefanie

Contents

Nightly Guide to Lunar Features

Foreword

Andrew Planck first came to my attention when he submitted to *Lunar Photo of the Day* an image of the lunar crater Pitatus and a photo of a pie he had made. Both the 60-mile diameter crater and the 10" wide pie are ringed by fractures that probably formed the same way. Gases associated with the lavas that filled the crater lifted its floor, which cooled and then collapsed with the fractures marking the breaking point. The pie crust did the same, with the gases coming from cherries rather than lavas. Although the pie is long gone, you will always think of it when observing Pitatus.

This comparison is characteristic of Andrew's practical approach to observing and understanding the Moon. His new observing guide, *What's Hot on the Moon Tonight?*, points out interesting targets to observe, night by night during the lunar month. There are descriptions of the craters, mountains, rilles and domes that you can see, but also brief explanations of the geologic processes that formed them. Understanding what you see makes observing far more interesting—it has certainly hooked me for more than 50 years.

Like the title, the writing in *What's Hot on the Moon Tonight?* is brisk and fun. Because many unfamiliar terms are needed to describe lunar features, Andrew includes a 35-page Glossary, which is really a misnomer. Rather than being simply a drudge of definitions, it is a series of mini-essays. *What's Hot* also includes 12 pages telling a little about some of the ancient and modern scientists whose names have been given to lunar features. You will learn, for example, that the monk who added the name Copernicus to the Moon did it as an insult by flinging the then controversial scientist's crater into the Ocean of Storms. The monk is forgotten, the fame of Copernicus is eternal.

Reading about the Moon is fine, but Andrew also encourages you to make notes from your observations by providing plenty of space to write down your observations, as well as circular forms so you can sketch what appears in the eyepiece. Being forced to fill in a blank space on a drawing drives you back to the eyepiece to look more carefully at every piece of the landscape, thereby increasing your familiarity and knowledge.

What are you waiting for? Grab your telescope, a pencil and this book for a personal tour of the magical world in our sky.

Charles Wood
Author of *The Modern Moon: A Personal View*
Creator of *Lunar Photo of the Day, LPOD.wikispaces.com*

Acknowledgments

First and foremost, I would like to thank my wife, Susan, who gives me inspiration to do creative things. She patiently supported and encouraged me through the several years it took to write this book. Susan also read the entire manuscript, red pencil in hand, and with a wife's unfailing instinct helped keep me subdued when I was tempted to stray during unbridled moments.

One day I serendipitously stumbled into a monthly writers' group that was conducted by Judith Briles (The Book Shepherd) in her home in Aurora, Colorado. Judith has a stunning amount of knowledge about writing and publishing and shares it freely at her monthly meet-ups. I was doubly fortunate in that her husband, John Maling (Editing By John) is a gifted professional editor and I promptly hired him to edit this book. I am enormously grateful to him for the work he did.

Judith and John recommended their friend and colleague Nick Zelinger (NZ Graphics) to do the book design. I am equally indebted to Nick for the superior work he did for the cover and interior design.

I would like to thank my friend, Sallie Greenwood, who is a writer and editor, for very kindly agreeing to look over the manuscript and make comments.

My long time astronomy buddy, Andy Robertson, also read the manuscript and corrected several glaring errors.

I am indebted to Charles Wood, author of *The Modern Moon: A Personal View*, for writing the Foreword, and along with Wes Higgins, giving me permission to use the photo of the crater Pitatus which was published on the *Lunar Photo of the Day* website for March 10, 2006 (*LPOD.wikispaces.com*)

My friend Brian Kimball of the Longmont Astronomical Society (an astrophotographer par excellence) allowed me to use several of his photos.

Dana Thompson of the Columbus Astronomical Society gave me permission to use his photo of the Lunar X, a little known phenomenon which appears only for a few hours on lunar Day 6.

I am indebted to Mike Siddoway, professor of mathematics at Colorado College, for working out the formula for personal eye resolution found in the *Glossary*.

Gray Photography of Corpus Christi, Texas, kindly provided the photo used in the "About the Author" section free of charge.

Unless otherwise noted, all other images are from NASA / USGS / BMDO / LROC / ASU / DLR / LOLA / Moon Globe. Used by permission.

How to Use this Guide

The Moon gets a bad rap. Although it is a thing of astonishing beauty and complexity, it is often looked upon by astronomers as a benevolent nuisance. It's great for poets and lovers, but it interferes with the viewing of faint fuzzy things that are millions of light years away. The feeble light from these objects is washed out by the Moon's glare, and astronomers will frequently not even bother to take out their telescopes when there is a Moon in the sky. In doing so, they deprive themselves of one of the richest and most fascinating views in the entire heavens. Paradoxically, if we could see Jupiter, Mars, and Saturn in the same detail that we see the Moon, we probably would never leave our telescopes!

The overriding purpose of this *Guide* is to encourage astronomers to look upon the Moon as a friend instead of an adversary. It is designed to enable the observer to sit at his or her telescope, turn to a particular day in the lunar month, and spend substantial time "walking" over the lunar surface observing, exploring, reading about, and understanding the history and formative processes of its various features. Both beginners and experienced astronomers will find this *Guide* to be enormously useful.

There are roughly 300,000 craters wider than 0.6 miles on the near side of the Moon.

The Moon is a delightful playground that will keep you fascinated for many years. Although some 10,000 craters larger than two miles in diameter are visible through amateur telescopes with at least a 6" aperture, this *Guide* is not merely a list of objects; it is designed to increase your enjoyment by increasing your understanding. It will teach you how to "read" the Moon as you are strolling about its surface with your telescope. Even a small 60mm telescope will show you an astonishing amount of detail. Take your time; don't be in a hurry. This is an opportunity to stop and smell the roses.

In addition to a telescope and this *Guide*, you will need a good map of the Moon (preferably *Sky & Telescope's Field Map of the Moon* available from *skyandtelescope.com* or *amazon.com*). The *Field Map* is the finest map of the Moon available and is designed to be used comfortably at the telescope. Lunar features that are described in this book are keyed to the *Sky and Tel's map*, and entries will look like this—Plato: [NW/D9]—meaning fold your *Field Map* to the northwest quadrant, grid location D9.[1] However, any map that has the features indexed will work.

Many of the features described are accompanied by thumbnail images to help you get oriented. I have deliberately kept these images small, as this should be a voyage of personal discovery. Your most exciting moments will come while you are at the eyepiece, not while you are looking at pictures.

If you have a smartphone or similar device, then take advantage of the several astronomy apps that are available on iTunes such as *SkySafari Plus*, *Deluxe Moon Standard*, *Lunatic*, *Moon Map Pro*, and *Moon Globe HD*.[2] As of this writing, only the first three will give you the critical **Lunar Day** for the evening that you plan to do your observing. Curiously, *Moon Map Pro* is the only app that gives the longitude of the **terminator**, a piece of information that will be

> Some early 60mm telescopes had gotten some undeserved bad press. My first telescope was a 60mm Tasco. Although it had a small aperture, once I invested in high quality eyepieces the telescope performed admirably and gave perfect diffraction patterns around stars. Fifty years and six telescopes later I still have (and use) that Tasco!

> The Moon takes about 29 days (from new Moon to new Moon) to cycle through its phases. These are referred to as Lunar Days 1-29. So, for example, if you wish to observe the Moon at first quarter you would turn to Day 7 in the *Field Guide*.

---

[1] If you're using a Newtonian reflector, simply turn the *Field Map* upside down. Other telescopes require some interpolation. A mirror image version is also available.

[2] These apps were available at the time of this writing, but apps come and go. However, you can depend on *SkySafari Plus* being around for a long time and, in addition, it is one of the finest astronomy programs available.

enormously helpful to you as you use this *Guide*.[3] The *Moon Globe HD* app renders the Moon with mind-boggling clarity! With it you will be able to zoom in on even the smallest craters without losing detail. (At full zoom you can see craters that are as small as one arc-second—the equivalent of viewing the Moon at around 250x.)

> It takes up to 30 minutes for your eyes to become dark adapted enough to allow you to see very faint objects. A careless burst of white light will destroy this in an instant, but red light will preserve your night vision.

Observing the Moon has several advantages over traditional astronomy, chief among which is that you can observe the Moon from the middle of a city through the worst of light pollution. And since you will be spending substantial time staring at a bright object, you may dispense with the obligatory red light. Use a white flashlight to consult this *Field Guide* and make notes. No more squinting is one of the many pleasant benefits of studying the Moon!

You can also begin your observing during the brighter portions of twilight, before any stars are visible. The Moon can even be observed profitably during the daytime. The lunar observer can usually get to bed at a decent hour.

The *Glossary* at the end is a great deal more than a simple definition of terms. It contains all the information you will need to get a basic understanding of the Moon: its formative processes, its history, how it came to be, the details of crater formation and of the other features that you will be observing. A rewarding cloudy night activity would be to sit down and read through the entire *Glossary*. Terms that you find in this *Guide* that are in **bold face** are covered in the *Glossary*.

The *Guide* begins on Day 1 of the lunar cycle (New Moon is essentially Day 0) and proceeds through Full Moon. With some exceptions, the days after Full Moon are not included because these objects have been covered earlier (e.g., objects near the **terminator** on Day 17 are the same objects that were covered

---

[3] The terminator is the line dividing the light and dark portions of the Moon. Features are seen in astonishing detail when they are within 10° of the terminator.

on Day 3). The only difference is that the terminator is on the other side of these features, and sunlight is streaming in from the opposite direction. So if you find, for example, that the Moon for Day 3 is too low on the horizon to see objects clearly, wait until Day 17 or 18 when the evening terminator will be in about the same position.

Immediately following each Day entry you will find a terminator number (T-number), which indicates the longitude of the terminator. Features on the Moon look quite dramatic when they are within 10° or so of this line. However, the T-number assumes that the Moon has no libration (the apparent rocking back and forth of the Moon) so, depending on the degree of libration, the actual longitude of the terminator on the night you are observing may vary up to 7° from the T-number that is listed.

> A circle is divided into 360°. A degree is divided into 60 arc-minutes, and one arc-minute equals 60 arc-seconds. (This is pretty small stuff—a pinhead at 100 yards subtends an angle of one arc-second.) A low-power eyepiece will typically show more than 30 arc-minutes (the width of the Full Moon).

Also keep in mind that the terminator creeps across the Moon at approximately 10 miles per hour (which corresponds roughly to 9 arc-seconds at the mean distance of the Moon). Accordingly, you might wish to go forward or backward in the *Field Guide* by one day. (If you use the *Moon Map Pro* app, it will tell you exactly where the terminator is on the evening you plan to observe, so just match that up with the T-numbers.)

I have made no attempt to list all of the objects that are visible on a particular lunar day; the observer would be overwhelmed by uninteresting minutia and this *Guide* would quickly lose its value. In a word (a very subjective word) if objects are listed, it is because I have found them interesting to look at, or there are unusual formative processes involved, or they have a story to be told. In many cases it will be a combination of all these things.

Although the most pertinent information has been included in the text proper, ancillary information will be diverted to footnotes, sidebars, the *Glossary*, and the appendices so that you won't be distracted from the enjoyment of viewing. Because many of the features on the Moon have been named after individuals who have changed the course of history, by the time you have finished observing for one lunar month and read all the attendant information, you will have, in effect, completed a mini-course in Western civilization.

Craters which are named after such persons have a symbol following their names, such as **Aristarchus:**†. This symbol directs you to *Appendix A: Historical Notes* where you can read about the contributions they have made.

As is the case with observing deep-sky objects, the more you look, the more you see. To this end, each facing page is a blank sheet with lines provided to make notes, do drawings, and encourage you to really *look*. (If you run out of space, there are extra blank pages provided at the end of the book plus an additional section consisting only of blank drawing circles.)[4] If you're like most people, the idea of "doing drawings" is an intimidating prospect. You probably don't bother because you think you have no talent and you'd rather spend your time observing than trying to finesse your inept squiggles into something your grandma would be proud of.

Here's the secret: Forget grandma—you're going for quick lines, circles and dots, nothing more! Spend no more than two minutes drawing a crater and its prominent features. The idea is to quickly record what you can see, then come back later and try to see more. Don't be surprised if, after a few sessions, you discover that you're looking forward to nights that are dominated by the Moon.

As you are planning a night's observation, it would be a good idea to read over the corresponding information for the Lunar Day in question beforehand so that you have an idea of what to look forward to. This would be particularly helpful if you are doing a public star party, as you will be prepared to speak knowledgeably about features that will be prominent that evening.

---

[4] Permission is hereby granted for you to make extra copies of these Notes pages as needed.

In any case, the next time you sit down at your telescope, open this *Guide* and read about the objects you are observing. Don't be in a hurry. Broaden your understanding and enjoy what you are looking at.

Happy viewing!

Map of Major Seas

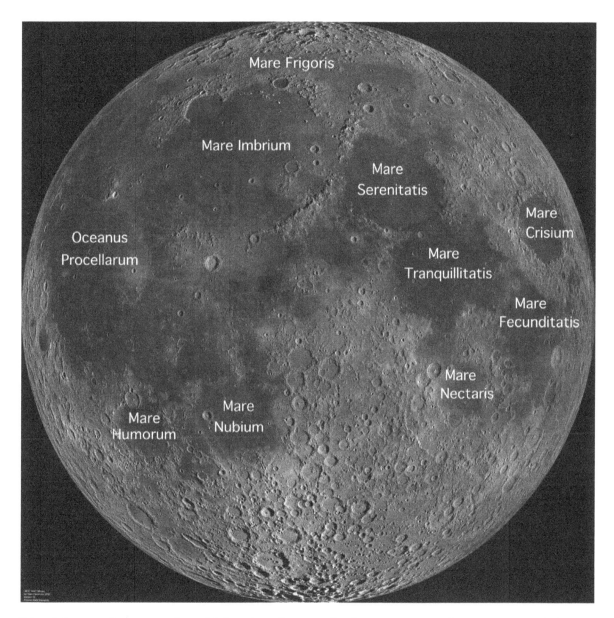

The Moon observer should be familiar with the names and positions of the 10 major seas: Crisium, Fecunditatis, Nectaris, Tranquillitatis, Serenitatis, Frigoris, Imbrium, Nubium, Humorum, and Oceanus Procellarum. (This is akin to finding your way around the sky by knowing the constellations.)

NOTES

_____

_____

_____

_____

_____

_____

_____

_____

_____

_____

_____

_____

_____

_____

_____

_____

_____

_____

Nightly Guide to Lunar Features

DAYS 1 & 2 (T=79°-68° E)[5]

Because the Moon is so very low on the horizon, Days 1 and 2 are really not worth the trouble. Wait until the first two days after Full Moon when you can see these features to greater advantage. However, some astronomers play a game of trying to spot the earliest possible Moon with the naked eye. The best time to view such a Moon is in March and April because the ecliptic (the apparent path of the Sun and planets against the starry background) is more perpendicular to the horizon. As a result, after the Sun sets, a closely trailing Moon will become visible in a dark sky more quickly than at other times in the year. After the Sun has set and twilight has begun, scan the area around the sunset point on the horizon for the Moon. **Do not attempt this until the Sun has completely set. Permanent eye damage *will* result if you accidentally view the sun through binoculars!**

Within Islamic cultures, spotting the earliest Moon is not a game but quite a serious part of their religion, as many of their practices cannot begin until the first sliver of a crescent Moon has been sighted.

Promontorium Agarum: [NE/H16] an impressive cape on the SE edge of Mare Crisium. It has peaks which rise to several thousand feet above its floor. **Lunar Transient Phenomena** (LTP's) have occasionally been reported in this region, especially right after sunrise.

LTP's are short-lived changes in lighting or color (either sudden or gradual). They manifest themselves as obscurations, foggy patches, etc.

---

[5] The "T-number" indicates the longitude of the terminator. (See *Glossary* for complete details.)

Humboldt: [SE/M18] This crater is best viewed when there is a pronounced libration. Because of foreshortening, it appears to be extremely elongated north to south. It has a cluster of central peaks, and if you're lucky you might spot a long catena (crater chain) extending from the northeast rim of the crater.

_____

_____

_____

_____

_____

_____

_____

_____

_____

_____

_____

_____

_____

_____

_____

_____

_____

_____

_____

DAYS 1 & 2

DAY 3 (T=59° E)

One of the loveliest views of the Moon can be seen around Day 3, and to appreciate it you don't even need a telescope. Go out in the evening of the third day, just as deep twilight is ending, and look west. The Moon will seem magically suspended over the horizon, and its dark side will be softly glowing from **earthshine**.[6] At such times the daylight portion of the Earth shines a beacon of reflected sunlight toward the Moon whose dark side acquires a lovely ethereal glow. We perceive this glow as *earthshine*. Spring is an especially good time to enjoy this sight. It is particularly lovely when Venus is suspended just next to the Moon, and if you can possibly add the aroma of nearby apple blossoms then you will have created a scene of transcendental beauty. It is a time for lovers and poets.

Aristarchus:† [NW/G5] The crater Aristarchus is the brightest spot on the Moon. It is so bright that Sir William Herschel[7] mistook it for an erupting volcano, and its glow can even be seen coming through on the dark side of the Moon around Day 3 when it is illuminated only by earthshine. While you're at it, see if you can spot segments of the Tycho ray system[8] which are also visible under earthshine.

Endymion: [NE/D15] This is an older crater which somewhat resembles Plato [Day 8; NW/D9] in that it has a smooth, dark-chocolate floor and three-mile-high walls which cast lovely shadow spires on the flood plain below when the Sun is low.

200 miles would be about three arc-minutes north of Crisium. Being familiar with the field of view (FOV) of your eyepieces will help you navigate.

---

[6] This is a monthly phenomenon referred to as *the old Moon in the New Moon's arms.*

[7] 18th c. English astronomer who discovered Uranus.

[8] See **splash rays** in the *Glossary*

Geminus: [NE/F15] Roughly 200 miles north of Mare Crisium (below) you will find the moderately complex 55-mile crater Geminus. It has terraced walls and small central peaks. This will give you an indication of what to start looking for in the following days as craters become increasingly more complex.

Burckhardt: [NE/F15] This is the crater with the "Mickey Mouse" ears. It is a remarkable exception to the rule that when one crater intrudes upon another, the younger crater (the intruder) is always smaller. Burckhardt has landed smack in between two smaller but older craters, giving it the Mickey Mouse effect.

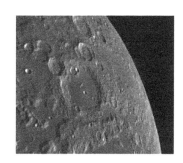

Cleomedes: [NE/G15] Cleomedes is the first significant crater just north of Mare Crisium. It is a splendid crater, 80 miles in diameter, with terraced walls, rilles, and a small central mountain. There are also two crater-lets, and a y-shaped rille on the northern half of the floor just east of the central mountain peak. Notice that the floor is unusually smooth. Because its southern rim touches one of the multi-rings encircling the Crisium basin, it is believed that lava rose up through Crisium fractures and smoothly covered the floor of Cleomedes. Under a low-angle Sun you might be able to detect that the rille cuts through a small dome on the northern section of the floor.

Mare Crisium: [NE/H15] On Day 3 the Sea of Crises, the first of the large seas to become visible on the waxing Moon, has now been fully revealed. We tend to think of craters as comparatively small objects and lose sight of the fact that large lunar "seas" are the result of crater impacts also. Basically, if it's round, it's a crater. Mare Crisium resulted from the impact of a large meteor 3.9 billion years ago. The event was energetic enough to leave a multi-ring imprint, parts of which we can clearly see. Notice the ring

features bending around Crisium on its north side. Particularly notice how Mare Anguis on the NE side of Crisium [G16] extends itself toward the west, passes below Cleomedes, and then dissipates at Tisserand. The Crisium basin appears elliptical, with its long axis running from north to south. This is an illusion due to the effects of foreshortening.

Crisium actually *is* elliptical, but, contrary to what your eyes tell you, its long axis runs east to west.

Take a mental image of how much space there is between Mare Crisium and the eastern rim of the lunar disk. This will vary from month to month, even from night to night, and will be an indicator of how much **libration** has come into play.

Once you have become familiar with the details on the surface of Mare Crisium, particularly around Promontorium Agarum, be on the lookout for LTP's.

These have been reported from time to time and manifest themselves as mists that mysteriously appear and obscure some of the surrounding details.

If you have the *Moon Globe HD* app, you can see the effects of fore-shortening for yourself. Do a search for Mare Crisium as it normally appears near the east limb of the Moon. Notice how it is elongated north to south. Then with one finger, move Crisium to the center of the screen and it will develop its true east-west elongation.

Dorsum Oppel: [NE/H15] As the lava cooled following the impact that created Mare Crisium, a series of **wrinkle ridges**, known as Dorsum Oppel, formed along the entire western edge and give the impression of waves lapping on the shore. The flowing lava partially filled the pre-existing craters Yerkes and Lick [H15], turning them into **ghost craters**.

There is also a more substantial ridge that connects the flooded crater Yerkes with the smaller Yerkes E, 15 miles to its northwest (unnamed on the *Field Map*). Under a low Sun, when the terminator is around 52°-55°, this ridge will combine with the SW rim of Yerkes to look remarkably like the silhouette of a bird in flight. It has consequently been nicknamed the Flying Eagle. (This feature may be seen to better advantage on Day 17 when the Sun is setting.)

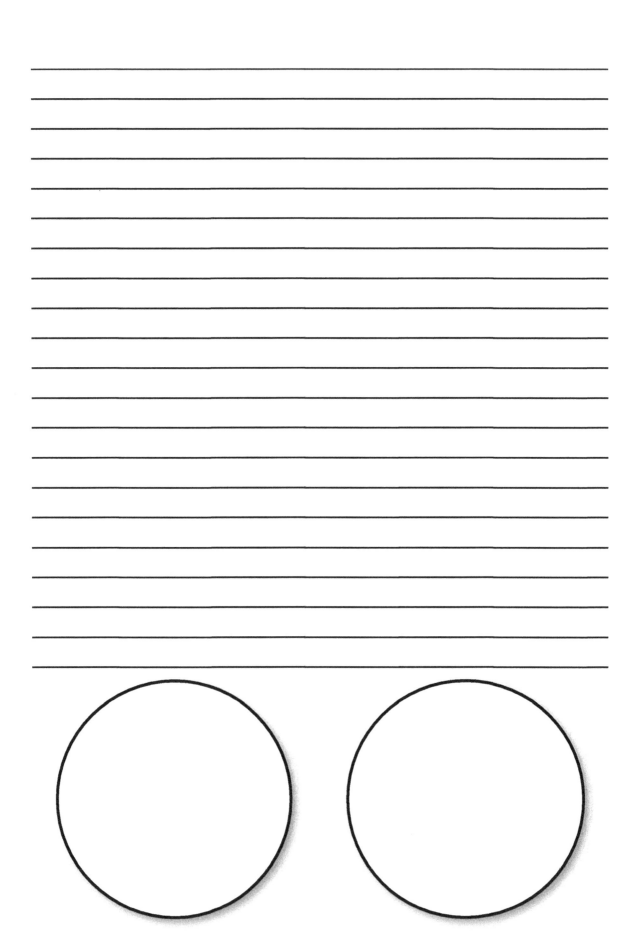

Peirce & Picard: [NE/H15] The two largest intact craters on Mare Crisium are Peirce and Picard. They are only about 12 miles in diameter by 1 mile deep and will require 75x-100x to see them. They are located on a more or less north-south line about 30 miles in from the western shore of Crisium (Peirce is the northern-most). The lava that covered Crisium stopped flowing before these craters formed. You should easily be able to spot Swift, a small seven-mi. crater just eight miles to the north of Peirce.

The Great Eastern Chain: [SE/K-N16] There is a conspicuous chain of large craters, at one time referred to as the Great Western Chain, which closely hugs the same meridian near the eastern limb (i.e., the rim of the visible disk) of the Moon. They start on the southeast-ern shore of the Sea of Fertility[9] and continue south. The

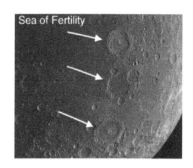

Sea of Fertility

chain consists of Langrenus, Vendelinus, Petavius, and Furnerius. These craters started to come into view last night. Although this unusual alignment is coincidental, it was once posited as evidence to support the **endogenic theory** of crater forma-tion—the now disproven theory that the majority of craters were formed by volcanic forces originating from within the Moon. (Come back on Day 16 when you'll be able to see them more clearly.)

Langrenus & Vendelinus: [SE/K-L16] These craters are the first two segments of the Great Eastern Chain (above). Langrenus and Vendelinus are two large 90-mi. craters located on the southeast shore of Fertility. One is considerably older than the other and appeared before the lava flows started. It should be easy for you to decide which is which.[10] The terraces and central peaks of Langrenus will have emerged from last night's shadows, and tonight the crater is a beautiful sight.

---

[9] Its official (and somewhat cumbersome) name is *Mare Fecunditatis*. I prefer the simplicity of "Fertility" and will use it throughout this guide.

[10] See *Crater Age* in the *Glossary*

Even if you have a small telescope, there is much detail in the interior and on the outer ramparts to keep you busy. Because the appearance of the crater changes significantly with different lighting angles, make some drawings of what it looks like tonight and come back over the next few nights to compare the views.

The younger crater Lamé intrudes on Vendelinus on its NE rim, and it is appropriately smaller. However, notice that Lamé, in turn, overlaps two smaller unnamed craters on its SW rim. This is unusual in that intruding craters are almost always smaller than the craters they impact on.

Petavius: [SE/M16] This is one of the most beautiful craters on the Moon, but it may be more profitably seen on Days 16 and 17 when the Moon is not so low on the horizon. It is an example of a **floor-fractured crater** (FFC), a type of crater that has been modified by later volcanism, uplift, and consequent fracturing. Because of the curvature of the lunar surface, the 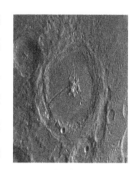 floor of Petavius is nearly 1,000 feet higher near its center than around the edge! Is the curvature apparent to you? Turbulence and volcanic upheaval from below split the central mountain (which rises to nearly one mile above the floor) and formed the rilles.

The principal rille on the floor, Rima Petavius, is so prominent that it can be seen with a 60mm refractor.[11] It is a **graben**, an elongated depression that results when stresses open up two parallel cracks in the lunar crust and the terrain in between drops. The rille extends from the central peak to the southwest wall. There are actually several rilles on the floor. How many can you see with your instrument?

Furnerius: [SE/N16] This is the last of the craters that make up the *Great Eastern Chain* and it is very old, having formed before the impact that created the Nectaris basin 3.9 billion years ago. Although the walls have been battered down and show

---

[11] i.e., the objective lens is 60mm (2.4") in diameter. This is the smallest telescope used for astronomy, but avoid buying one so small. Go for at least a 6" Newtonian, or better still, an 8".

their age, there are still many complexities remaining which will reward careful observation. There are several craterlets of varying sizes on the floor of Furnerius, including a 30-mile rille extending from the north rim toward the southeast. **Patrick Moore** reports that there are fourteen large craters and several craterlets in its

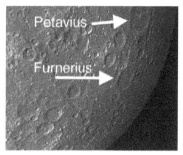

interior. (A more reasonable assessment would be there is one large crater and several craterlets.) Make a rough sketch of how many you can see, then come back next month (and on Day 17) to see if you can add to the count.

Can you match Patrick Moore's observing skills?

Leibnitz Mountains: [SE/T13] Follow the terminator all the way south and continue a short way beyond the end of the crescent. If you're lucky, you'll see tiny star-like points of light shining in the dark just off the limb of the Moon. These are the tops of the Leibnitz Mountains, a range so high that at 36,000 feet one of its peaks, Leibnitz β (Beta), the highest mountain on the Moon, would tower above Mt. Everest! Unfortunately the Leibnitz Mountains are not well placed for viewing, but it's worth trying to get a peek at the Moon's highest mountain.

_____

_____

_____

_____

_____

_____

_____

_____

_____

_____

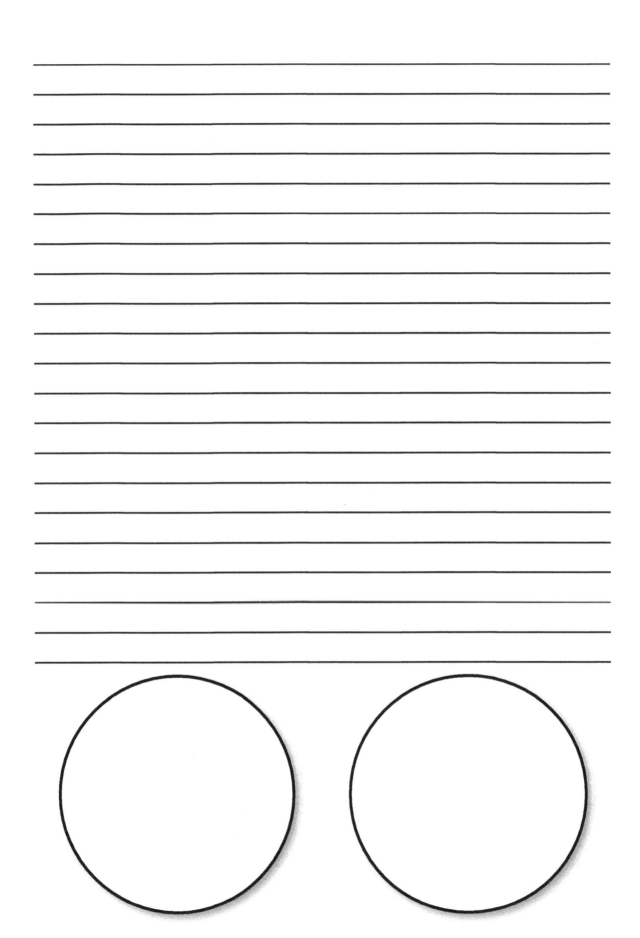

Day 4 (T=45° E)

Hercules and Atlas:† [NE/E13-14] Just east of Lacus Mortis (the "Lake of Death") are two splendid craters, Hercules and Atlas. They have been described variously as "noble, magnificent, spectacular, scarcely surpassed." Although in Greek mythology, Atlas and Hercules were contemporaries, the craters named after them appeared at widely different times. You should be able to tell at a glance which crater is older. (See **crater age** in the *Glossary*.)

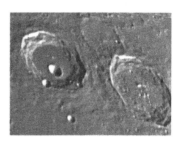

Atlas has central peaks, rilles, a hummocky floor, and two small dark halos known as lunar *pyroclastic deposits*. It is also one of the Moon's many examples of a *floor-fractured crater* (FFC).

Hercules has multiple terraces, and if you look very closely at it under the right lighting you will notice two small bumps that are reminiscent of the crater *Cassini*, which you will encounter on Day 7 [E10]. These tiny bumps, located just north of the large internal crater *Hercules G*, are actually the tops of enormous mountains that have been almost entirely inundated by prolific lava flows. Hercules is also the site of reported **transient lunar phenomena** (LTP's).

Did you notice that both Atlas and Hercules have blankets of surrounding ejecta, known as a glacis?

Rupes Cauchy: [NE/J13] (This may not be observable until Day 5 but is mentioned here because the nearby Cauchy domes must be observed at early lunar sunrise.) Two of the best-known faults on the Moon are *Rupes Cauchy* and *Rupes Recta* [Day 8; SW/M9]. They are fascinating to explore and they share remarkably similar neighborhoods: Both features are paralleled by a nearby rille, and in each case an intervening small crater separates the rille and the fault.

Seven miles northeast of Cauchy crater you will find Rima Cauchy, a rille that is 130 miles long, 2½ miles wide, and twists itself into a tight double u-turn halfway between Cauchy crater and the rille's northwest end.

To the southwest of Cauchy is the 75-mile Rupes Cauchy, an impressive fault that actually changes into a rille at both ends. The changeover point occurs coincidentally at two small craters that mark where the fault line starts to curve slightly to the southwest. Look carefully and see if you can detect the difference between a *rima* (a long groove) and a *rupes* (a cliff). This will be more obvious at lunar sunrise as the Moon's surface is higher on the northeast side of the fault and a conspicuous shadow will be cast toward the west. On Day 18 the setting Sun brightly illuminates the westward-facing slope of the fault. Because these two features are radial to the *Serenitatis Basin,* they are probably associated with stresses that resulted from the Serenity impact nearly 3.9 billion years ago.

Cauchy domes: [NE/J13] During sunrise over this area you will have an opportunity to view the first of your lunar domes, low rounded features that resulted from magma which rose from underneath and created blister-like hills on the Moon's surface.

Smaller objects surrounding a main feature are identified by adding a Greek letter to its name; hence, the dome Cauchy ω (omega) is considered a subsidiary feature to Cauchy crater.

Sometimes the lava actually burst out of the tops of these domes and you can still see the resulting vents. Both types of domes can be seen here just south of Rupes Cauchy.

Can you see the tiny crater pit on top of Cauchy ω (omega), the dome to the east?

Taruntius: [NE/J14] Located on the north shore of Fertility, Taruntius is a wonderful example of a **floor-fractured crater** (FFC). Take a close look at it. Once you are familiar with the appearance of "normal" craters, you will notice right away that Taruntius has an unusually shallow basin.

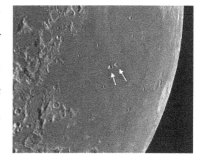

This is because hot magma underneath pushed upward with such force that the entire floor rose a little over a mile to its present level!

Also notice the surrounding material that was ejected from the impact (the secondary craters) and the small crater *Cameron* that resulted from an object that hit precisely on the northwest rim! (Although *Cameron* looks small, it is nearly seven times larger than **Meteor Crater** in Arizona!)

Mare Fecunditatis

Messier:† [SE/K14] One of my favorite objects on the Moon is a small pair of craters named Messier and Messier A. They are located on the western lava plains of the Sea of Fertility and can be easily seen through the smallest telescopes. The craters have a pair of **splash rays** that resemble the tails of a comet (an appropriate resemblance, considering who they are named after).

These rays, which extend about 75 miles to the west, have a happy characteristic in that they are visible under lower angles of illumination. It is unusual to be able to see both a crater and the rays it produced at the same time. (See Tycho on Day 8 [SW/P8], the most conspicuous example of splash rays.)

The most commonly accepted explanation of the origin of this unusual feature is that a projectile came in at a low angle (1° to 5°) from the east, smashed into the Moon to excavate Messier, and then ricocheted. When it landed the second time *Messier A* was formed, along with its attendant "comet tails." The projectile's extremely low angle of approach explains the oblong shape of the craters. Notice that the Messier impact created a butterfly pattern, typical of very low-angle impacts, while the ejecta from Messier A formed the two comet tails.

Charles Messier discovered so many comets during his career that he was dubbed "The Ferret of Comets" by King Louis XV of France.

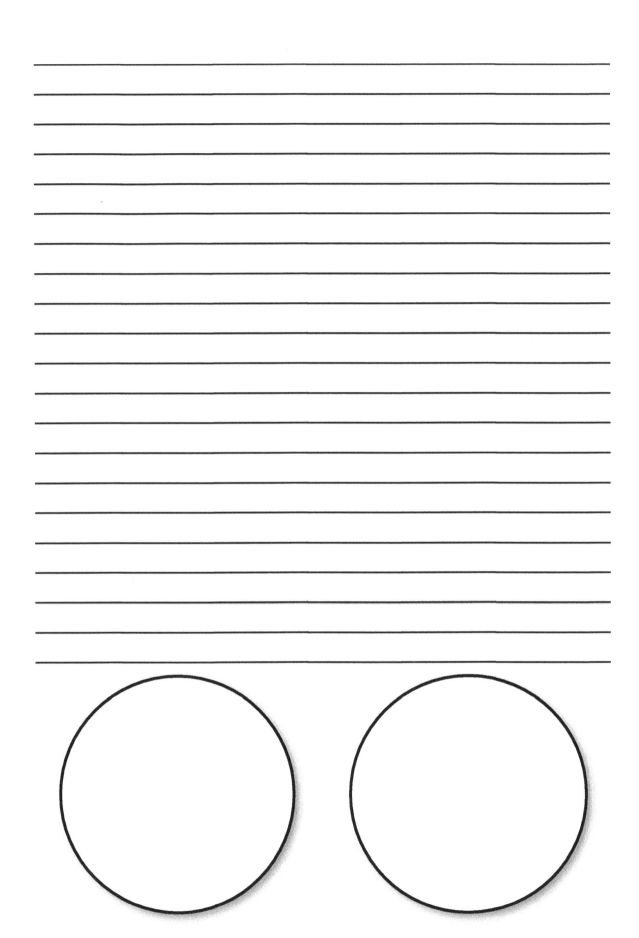

Gutenberg:† [SE/K14] While you're in the area, drop by and pay your respects to one of history's great men. Gutenberg crater is not only of historical importance because of its namesake, it shows an unusual sequence of crater development. Gutenberg is a large crater (45 mi. in diameter) that is intruded upon by a smaller crater (12 mi. in diameter— Gutenberg E) on its eastern wall. So far so good. But take a close look at the crater immediately adjoining it to the south (Gutenberg C). These craters have violated the usually dependable rule that newer craters are smaller than the older craters they have intruded upon. Gutenberg C is the older crater, while the larger Gutenberg is the interloper.

Another item of interest is the small bowl-shaped crater on the southwest rim (Gutenberg A). If you read about simple craters in the *Glossary*, then you know that the rim shadow on a bowl-shaped floor will appear as a smooth arc. If the floor is flat because it has been partially filled in with boulders that have tumbled down the crater's walls, the shadow will be truncated (i.e., the apex will be squared off). Can you tell if the floor of Gutenberg A is bowl-shaped or flat?

Mare Nectaris: [SE/L13] The Nectaris basin was excavated 3.9 billion years ago. The oldest features on the Moon formed prior to this event. Mare Nectaris is a classic example of a multi-ring basin. Tonight or tomorrow night will reveal Rupes Altai, a

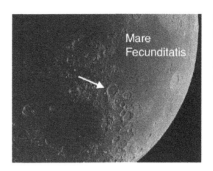

Mare Fecunditatis

DAY 4

When I was a youngster and first observed Messier and Messier A, the two craters were known as Messier and Pickering. I was fascinated by the pair and bought into the romantic notion (which was being proposed at the time) that the formation represented a tunnel that had been blasted through a mountain range by a low flying meteor. When the cold light of modern science revealed that this was not the case, I was crushed. (I have not yet recovered from the disappointment.)

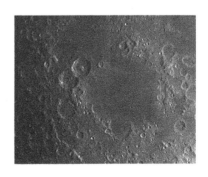

high cliff that is a conspicuous fragment of one of the original rings. As daylight moves across the region, try to locate hints of other ring features surrounding Mare Nectaris.

DAY 4

Vallis Rheita: [SE/N14] At 276 miles, the Rheita Valley is the longest distinct valley on the Moon. If you look closely at this formation, you will see that it is not a valley in the traditional sense but is made up of a series of interlocking craters whose alignment significantly points back to Mare Nectaris,

their place of origin. When the Nectaris basin was blasted out 3.9 billion years ago, more than a dozen mountain-sized chunks of debris took flight in a curiously straight line, and when they landed they ploughed out a 240-mi. long trough which we enjoy observing today as the Rheita Valley.

At the northeast end of Rheita Valley you will find the 45-mi. crater for which it was named. It is not difficult to figure out which came first, the crater or the valley. See what you think.

Although the Moon usually appears absolutely flat, this sector of the Moon gives you a noticeable three-dimensional effect as Rheita Valley diminishes into the distance around the curve of the Moon.[12]

> The Rheita Valley is as long and as wide as the Grand Canyon. The difference is that the Grand Canyon took millions of years to form. The Rheita Vally took only seconds!

---

[12] During a lunar eclipse you will frequently notice a striking three-dimensional effect as light being refracted through the atmosphere on opposite sides of the Earth strike the lunar surface from different angles.

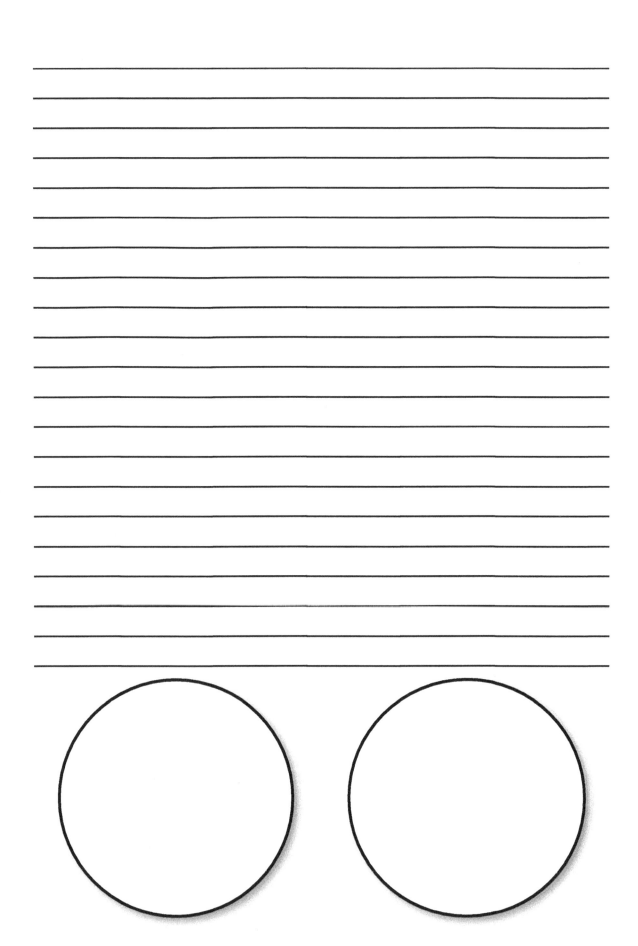

Day 5 (T=24° E.)

Lacus Mortis: [NE/E12] (The Lake of the Dead) This is a large lava-flooded crater (90 miles in diameter) just north of Mare Serenitatis which contains **rilles, wrinkle ridges, faults,** and a substantial internal crater, Bürg. At more than four billion years, Lacus Mortis is one of the oldest impact features on the Moon. The principal rille, Rima Bürg, is 60 miles long and can be seen through small telescopes. Another rille starts halfway between Bürg and the western rim of the Lacus and goes straight south. In the process it changes from a generic rille to a genuine fault whose floor falls away on the western side. At sunrise you will see a shadow extending to the west, and at sunset (around

Day 19) the face of the fault is brightly illuminated. Make a quick sketch of Lacus Mortis, then come back later and see if you can add more detail.

Bürg: [NE/E12] The centerpiece of Lacus Mortis is the 25-mile crater Bürg, a complex crater with terraces and a central mountain peak that appears to be split in two. As far as complex craters go, Bürg is a bit unusual. Instead of being mostly circular, the rim is scalloped and wavy and there is an inordinate amount of slumping on the western interior slopes; a finger of the slumping actually touches the central mountain peak! Some observers have reported a small summit pit on the top of the central mountain.

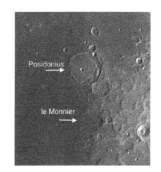

Posidonius

le Monnier

Posidonius/le Monnier: [NE/F-G13] There are only two craters of any consequence on Mare Serenitatis: Posidonius (named after a Greek astronomer/philosopher, not the god of the sea) and le Monnier. They are both textbook

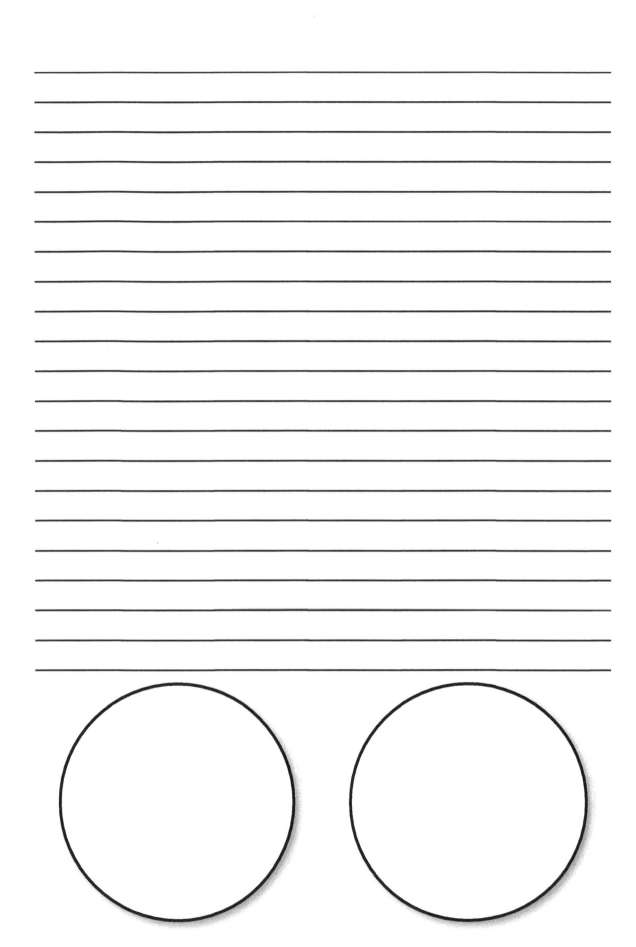

examples of **subsidence**, but Posidonius is, in addition, a **floor-fractured crater** (FFC). It has internal craterlets and a complex system of rilles, so you get more bang for your buck. (For its near twin, see Gassendi—Day 10.) Its substantial ramparts, which have been inundated by lava flows on the western side, are evident to the east and south of the crater's rim. If you can make out the north-south rille on the western side of the basin floor, does it appear to curve around to the east just inside the rim, or does it cleave its way through the mountains (as it appears to do in some photographs)? How does it strike you? Spend some time with Posidonius, it has a lot to teach. (Read about subsidence and FFC's in the *Glossary*, then come back to enjoy these two craters.)

Serpentine Ridge: [NE/G12] West of Posidonius in the Sea of Serenity you will find the Moon's best example of a wrinkle ridge. Like breaking waves that sometimes indicate reefs lying just under the surface of the water, wrinkle ridges often signal the presence of subsurface structures on the Moon. Serpentine Ridge reveals the

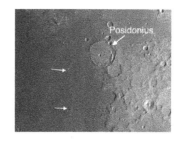

ghostly outlines of an underlying mountain range that formed the inner ring of the Serenity basin.[13] At the highest point of this ridge, just west of Posidonius where it looks like the ridge splits into a "Y," there is a tiny 1.2-mi. crater that will test both your optics and the seeing conditions.

Dawes:[14] [NE/H12] Positioned in the straits between Tranquillity and Serenity is the small 11-mile crater *Dawes*. Some observers say it has a small central peak, others do not. What do you think?

"Serpentine Ridge" is the picturesque name that amateur astronomers have been using since the 1800s. However, in 1976 the International Astronomical Union officially changed the name to "Dorsa Smirnov" (which is a good example of why astronomers don't make good poets).

---

[13] See basins under *crater morphology* in the *Glossary*.

[14] Of *Dawes Limit* fame. (See *Glossary*)

Arago: [NE/J12] About 50 miles from the western shore of Tranquillity you will find the crater Arago (16 mi.). This is an unusual crater. In the place of a central peak you will see a substantial ridge that extends from the center of Arago's floor to its northern rim. The evidence suggests that there was a significant collapse of rim material which simply merged with the central peak.

Arago domes: [NE/J12] On Day 4 you got your first introduction to lunar domes around the crater Cauchy. Now you can broaden on the experience. Arago has a pair of very large domes, one to its north (Arago α [Alpha]) and one to its west (Arago β [Beta]). These are two of the largest and most prominent domes on the Moon, and

halfway between Arago α and the crater Maclear (100 miles to its northeast) you will find a challenging group of four smaller domes. It will be a nice victory for you if you manage to spot them.

Rupes Cauchy: [Repeated from Day 4—NE/J13] Two of the best known faults on the Moon are Rupes Recta [Day 8; SW/M9] and Rupes Cauchy. They are fascinating to explore and they share remarkably similar neighborhoods: Both features are paralleled by a nearby **rille**, and in each case the rille and the fault are separated by an intervening small crater.

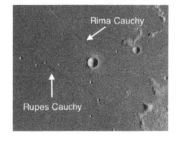

Northeast of Cauchy crater (7 mi.) you will find Rima Cauchy, a rille that is 130 miles long, 2½ miles wide, and twists itself into a tight double "u-turn" halfway between Cauchy crater and the rille's northwest end. To the southwest of Cauchy is the 75-mile Rupes Cauchy, an impressive fault that actually changes into a rille at both ends. The changeover point occurs coincidentally at two small craters that mark where the fault line starts to curve slightly to the southwest. Look carefully and see if you can detect the difference between a *rima* (a long

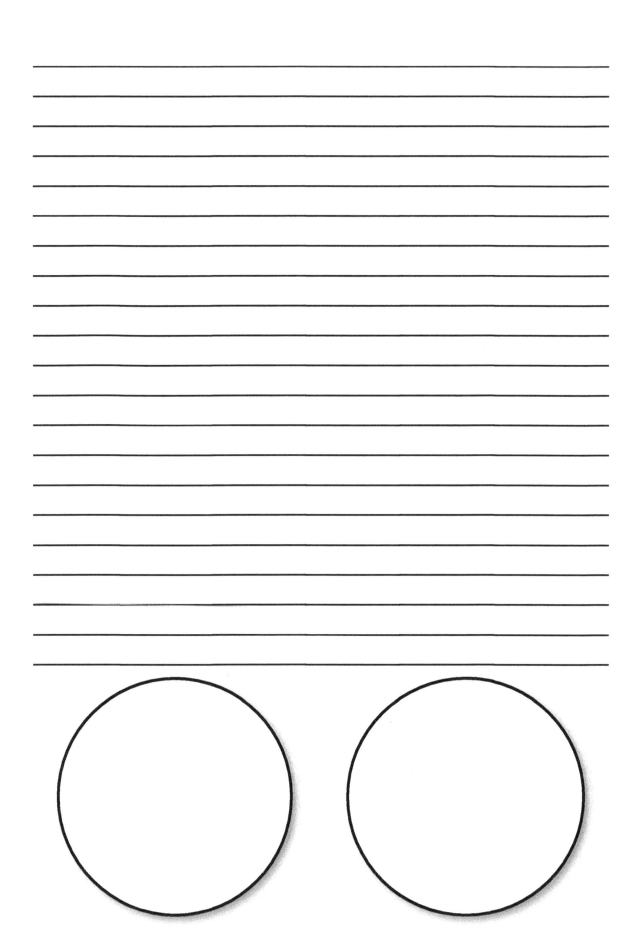

groove) and a *rupes* (a cliff). This will be more obvious at lunar sunrise as the Moon's surface is higher on the northeast side of the fault and a conspicuous shadow will be cast toward the west. On Day 18, the setting Sun brightly illuminates the westward-facing slope of the fault. Because these two features are radial to the *Serenitatis Basin*, they are probably associated with stresses that resulted from the Serenity impact nearly 3.9 billion years ago.

Cauchy domes: [Repeated from Day 4—NE/J13] (Depending on the libration, these domes may have been better observed last night.) During sunrise over this area you will have an opportunity to view the first of your 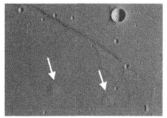 lunar domes, low rounded features that resulted from magma which rose from underneath and created blister-like hills on the Moon's surface. Sometimes the lava actually burst out of the tops of these domes and you can still see the resulting vents. Both types of domes can be seen here just south of Rupes Cauchy. Can you see the tiny crater pit on top of Cauchy ω (omega), the dome to the east?

Plinius: [NE/H12] Standing sentinel between Tranquillity and Serenity is the crater Plinius, a fine object with a sharp rim, terraces, an ejecta blanket, and a central projection which, depending on the illumination, has been described variously as a mountain, a double-mountain, central craters, or low mounds. How does it strike you?

Immediately to the north of Plinius are three prominent rilles (*Rimae Plinius*), which follow along the edge of the Serenity basin. The lava that filled Serenity was so heavy that it not only affected Posidonius and le Monnier, as described above, but more than 200 miles away substantial cracks opened up near Plinius.

Although the lavas covering Serenity have a brighter hue, can you see that the lava plains of Mare Tranquillitatis are darker and older? The coloring becomes suddenly lighter just north of Plinius.

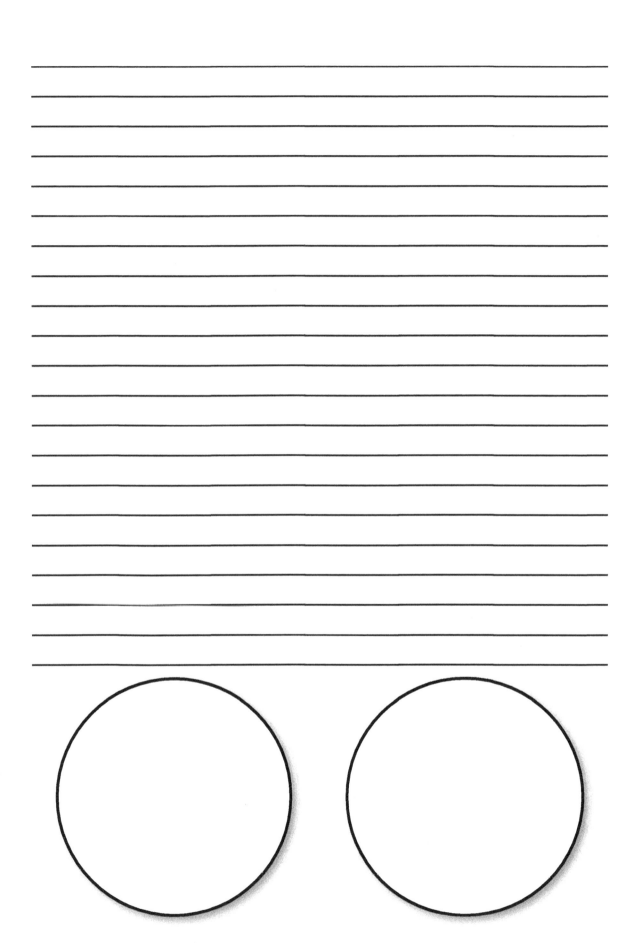

Ariadaeus: [NE/J11] The Ariadaeus Rille (Rima Ariadaeus—visible tomorrow night) is named after this 7-mi. crater located near its eastern end. Notice that the crater has a slightly smaller companion touching it on its northeast side. Their rims are gently pushing in on each other. Can you tell which one is older?

Lamont: [NE/J12] About 100 miles (1.5 arc-minutes) off the western shore of Tranquillity is a remarkable series of **wrinkle ridges**. You need to view them under a low Sun around Day 5 or 6.

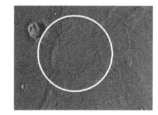

Lamont is the ghostly remnant of a small **multi-ring impact basin** that has been covered up by subsequent lava flows, but if this is so, it doesn't fit in with the standard sequence of crater morphology. Multi-rings do not generally appear until a crater attains a diameter of around 200 miles. If you catch it at the right time, the image of the underlying basin and rings show up remarkably well on the surface of Tranquillitatis.

Apollo 11: [NE/J12] The best time to see the *Apollo 11* landing site is around Day 5 or 4-5 days after Full Moon. You will find the landing site just east of the crater Sabine. In the close-by neighborhood are three tiny craters named for the astronauts of *Apollo 11*: Aldrin, Collins, and Armstrong. These craters can be used to test your telescope optics and the seeing conditions. From west to east, the crater diameters are: Aldrin (2.1 miles), Collins (1.5 miles) and Armstrong (2.9 miles).

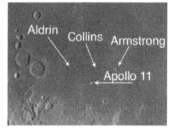

I am frequently asked if it is possible to see the flag on the Moon. The short answer is no. Since a 3-ft. flag at the distance of the Moon subtends an angle of 4.7×10^{-4} arc-seconds, it would require a telescope with a mirror that is roughly 800 feet in diameter (the size of 2½ football fields!) and a magnification of 500,000 merely to see the flag as a dot.

To magnify it to the point where it is recognizable as a flag, your telescope mirror would have to be 3.5 miles in diameter with a magnification of 11 million!

Sabine & Ritter: [NE/J11] About 60 miles west of the Apollo 11 landing site you will see two curious craters: Sabine and Ritter. They are unusual because they should be deeper than they are. Look closely at Sabine (the eastern-most) and you will see that its shallow floor looks like it has been cut out by a giant cookie cutter. Both

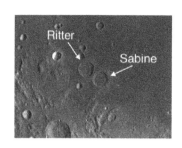

Sabine and Ritter are **floor-fractured craters** (FFC's). The pressure of upwelling magma from underneath has actually raised the floors to their present unnatural level.

Moltke: [NE/K12] Just south of the Apollo 11 site is Moltke (4 miles in diameter—about 4 arc-seconds), a perfect example of a *simple crater* with a smooth bowl.

Theophilus, Cyrillus, Catharina: [SE/L12] This is the most imposing trio of craters on the Moon. They are located just west of Mare Nectaris and have their own distinct personalities. Theophilus is a spectacular formation with all of the attendant complexities of a **Tycho-class**

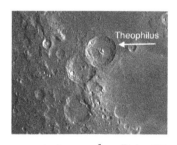

crater: terraced walls, a flat floor, and magnificent central mountain peaks. It is 60 miles in diameter, and the drop from the highest mountains on the rim to the floor below is a breathtaking 2.7 miles! Observers have reported that the shape of the central mountain seems to change as the lunation progresses. Keep a watch on Theophilus over the next few nights and see if you agree.

Notice how the floor of Theophilus is much smoother than the floors of Cyrillus and Catharina. When the impact occurred that produced Theophilus, much of the material that was excavated shot straight up. When it returned (in the form of molten rocks and mountain-sized boulders), it resurfaced the floor with a smooth veneer of lava.

There is also **Impact melt** around the crater exterior that can be easily seen with backyard telescopes. Take advantage of this, as there are not many places on the

"Slosh" is such a gentle term. It is commonly used to describe the Theophilus event, but it reminds us only of the last time we carelessly handled a cup of coffee. Now imagine yourself as an astronaut standing on the rim of Theophilus whose entire floor, nearly three miles below, is bubbling with hot lava. Suddenly huge sections of the far wall, 60 miles away, detach themselves and slam into the lake, raising a tidal wave of lava so high that it will crash over the cliff you are standing on and flood the plains to the north for another 60 miles. "Slosh" is probably not the first word that would come to mind.

Moon where you can see such a thing. Most of this impact melt occurs to the north of the crater and flows into *Sinus Asperitatis*. Lunar scientist Charles Wood points out that this is because the south rim is higher. Shortly after impact, the terraces collapsed into the lake of molten rock below which sent tidal waves of hot lava racing toward the opposite side. Because the north rim is lower, the material slammed into the wall, sloshed over the rim and pooled on the north side as impact melt.

Can you figure out the comparative ages of the three craters?[15]

Mare Nectaris: [Repeated from Day 4—SE/L13] The Nectaris basin was excavated 3.9 billion years ago. The oldest features on the Moon formed prior to this event. Mare Nectaris is a classic example of a multi-ring basin. Tonight should fully reveal the Altai Scarp (below), a conspicuous fragment of one of the original rings. As daylight moves across the region, try to locate hints of other ring features surrounding Mare Nectaris.

Fracastorius: [SE/M13] Located on the south shore of Mare Nectaris, this is one of the Moon's best examples of subsidence. The Nectaris lavas were so heavy that the floor

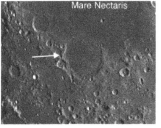

---

[15] Theophilus is younger than Cyrillus because it intrudes upon the latter's rim.
Catharina seems to be the oldest because there are five craters superimposed on it, and two elongated craters on its northeast rim point back toward Mare Imbrium, suggesting that Catharina is even older than Imbrium!

of Fracastorius actually cracked as it bent downward and allowed the Nectaris lavas
to flow over its northern rim. If you're lucky and have good optics and good seeing,
you might actually glimpse the unnamed rille that crosses the floor from east to
west just south of the center. There is a tiny 2.5-mi. crater right in the middle of this
rille that may help you spot it. (Daguerre on the north shore [L13] and its adjoining unnamed neighbor have both fallen victim to the same process of subsidence.)

There are some quite small objects on the floor of Fracastorius requiring high-
quality optics and steady seeing. How many of these can you detect? Make a quick
sketch, then come back later to compare.

Altai Scarp (*Rupes Altai*): [SE/M12] Viewable even
through small telescopes, the *Altai Scarp* is a spectacular
example of how shock waves from a major impact can
compress the surrounding terrain into a series of outwardly expanding rings. Nearly 3.9 billion years ago a
large asteroid or comet slammed in to the Moon and
dug out the Nectaris Basin. Shock waves rapidly expanded

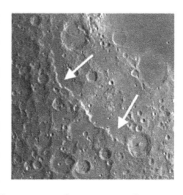

through the surrounding terrain and became frozen in place, producing a classic
multi-ring basin. Rupes Altai is a beautiful and conspicuous fragment of the
original rings. In truth, it is a circular mountain range whose highest peaks
rise to 13,000 feet! But you must catch the scarp under an early morning Sun,
it's majesty fades quickly. View it on Day 5 when the face of the scarp is fully
illuminated, then revisit the area around Day 19 or 20 at lunar sunset. At this time
the scarp sends long shadows over the terrain to the east. Which day shows the
scarp to its best advantage? (See ***multi-ring basins*** in the *Glossary*.)

As daylight moves across the region, try to locate hints of other ring features
surrounding Mare Nectaris.

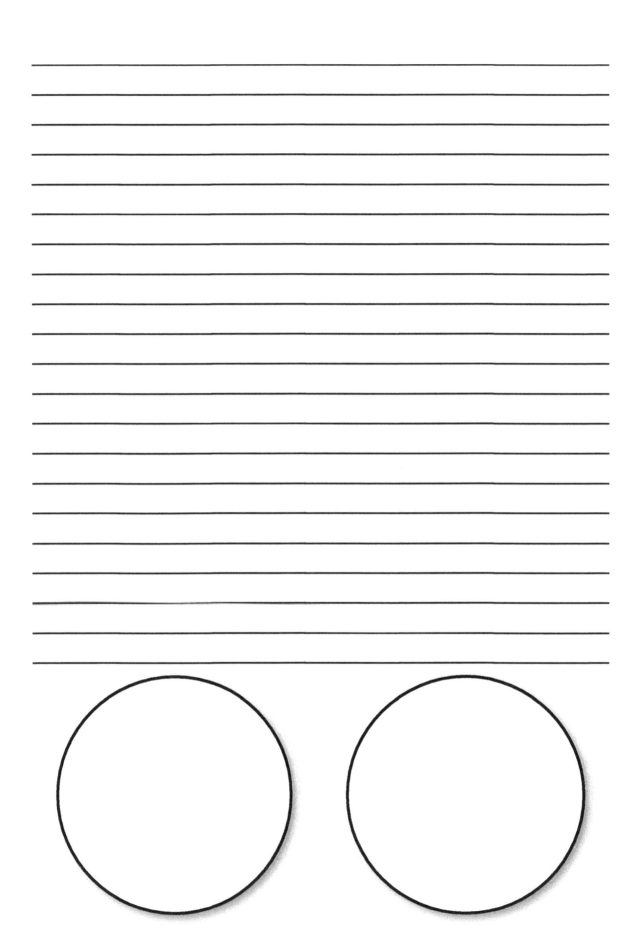

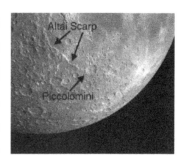

Piccolomini: [SE/M13] The Altai Scarp terminates on its southern end at Piccolomini (55 mi. in diameter), a beautiful and complex crater with a substantial central mountain peak, terraces, and a smooth convex floor. Notice how there is a great deal more turmoil around the southern rim of Piccolomini. Can you see the tiny craterlet just touching the northwest base of the central mountain? (If it is still in the mountain's shadow, try again tomorrow night or on Day 19.)

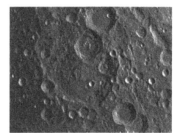

Janssen: [SE/P13] Janssen is located 85 miles southwest of the Rheita Valley (which you observed last night). Janssen's diameter is a robust 120 miles (Copernicus, the "Queen" of all craters, is a "mere" 58 miles in diameter!).

Janssen is a textbook example of how new craters are superimposed on top of older craters and, at the same time, are smaller than the older craters that underlie them.

Although Janssen is very old and its walls are in ruins, you should pay it a visit. When the Sun is low, it's rather like visiting the ruins of an old castle; it's still full of artifacts and reminders of a bygone age. The remains of the walls are still visible and there are mountains, rilles, and well-defined craters on its interior. The largest intruder is the crater *Fabricius* (48 mi.) that occupies the northern portion of the floor. The most impressive rille, *Rima Janssen*, is visible through very small telescopes. It appears to be a graben that curves conspicuously from the southwest wall of Janssen and attaches to the south wall of Fabricius. It is unusual in that it is a highland rille. Janssen is a rewarding field to play in. Revisit it often!

Day 6 (T=10° E)

Aristoteles: [NE/D11] Close to the terminator this evening there is an eye-catching pair of craters, Aristoteles and Eudoxus. Aristoteles is a complex crater with terraces, and in place of a central mountain it has a couple of small off-center peaks that are poking through the lava plain on its floor. The substantial ejecta blanket to the north of Aristoteles clearly shows radial structure, and if you catch it in the early morning sunrise it will look like many points of light peeking through the shadows.

Aristoteles adjoins the crater Mitchell to its immediate east. The pair violates the standard rule that smaller, younger craters must be superimposed on top of larger, older craters. Can you tell that the younger (and larger) Aristoteles is intruding onto Mitchell (which is older and smaller)?

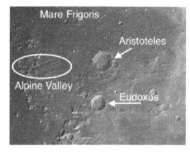

Eudoxus: [NE/E11] Both Eudoxus and Aristoteles to its north are wonderfully complex craters with terraced walls. Look closely at the pair. It's subtle, but can you see any features that would suggest which is older?[16] Just to the northeast of Eudoxus are three simple craters. Can you tell if their floors are bowl-shaped or flat?

The floors of bowl-shaped simple craters are round and their shadows will be curved. If enough debris has fallen from the crater walls to create flat floors, the shadows will be truncated, i.e., the apex will be squared off.

---

[16] The south wall of Aristoteles has been damaged and pushed in by debris that was ejected from the impact that created Eudoxus.

Valentine Dome: [NE/F11] Keep a close eye on the movement of the terminator, and when it just touches the western shore of Serenity (you may have to wait until tomorrow night) you will be able to make out a 20-mile wide volcanic dome located in what passes for the Straits of Serenity—the gap in the mountains where Serenitatis

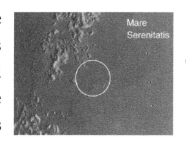

seems to flow into Mare Imbrium. This is an unusually large dome that must be caught under a low Sun. Although it does not have an official name, it is popularly referred to as the Valentine Dome because under certain lighting conditions it has a heart shape. Sitting atop the dome are three conspicuous hills (which are accompanied by six smaller ones). They are difficult to see but worth a try.

Linné: [NE/G11] Linné is a simple, relatively young crater with an interesting history. It is only 1.5 miles in diameter (about 1.3 arc-seconds at the average distance of the Moon), which makes it about twice the size of Meteor Crater in Arizona. Linné is surrounded by very light-colored material, and, because its appearance changes so much with different angles of illumination, this was once taken as evidence that the Moon was not a totally dead place. In 1866 it was erroneously reported that Linné had vanished. The idea caught on and was cited as proof that the Moon was still geologically active. Observe Linné under different lighting angles and see if you can convince yourself (if you didn't know better) that Linné could disappear. Observe it over the next few days, then come back at Full Moon and compare.

Mare Vaporum: [NE/H10] If the terminator has withdrawn sufficiently (you may have to wait until tomorrow night), notice how there are finger-like projections extending from the back side of the Apennines into Mare Vaporum. It is not coincidental that these extensions point back to Mare Imbrium, as they are part of the ejecta that was thrown out during the initial impact. (This also makes the Sea of Vapors considerably younger than Mare Imbrium.)

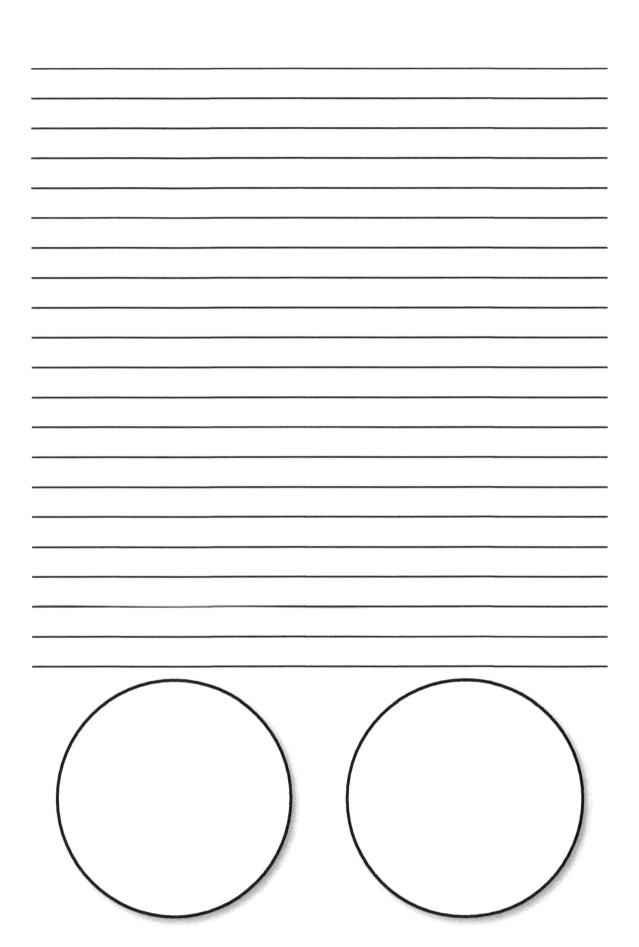

Proclus: [NE/H14] Proclus is a small crater located just west of Mare Crisium. In spite of its size it is one of the brightest spots on the Moon. When you view it around Full Moon you will notice it also has a system of rays that delicately fan out in a telltale butterfly-wing pattern, which tells you a lot about the flight path of the incoming projectile. Proclus is one of the best examples of what happens during a low-angle impact. (See *ejecta* and *butterfly patterns* in the *Glossary*.)

Julius Caesar: [NE/J11] Drop down to the Sea of Tranquillity and locate the partially ruined crater Julius Caesar near the western shore of Tranquillitatis. The floor of this crater is unusual in that it gradually darkens as you go north until it becomes one of the darkest areas on the surface of the Moon. The lighter-hued portion of the floor (and of the surrounding area) is believed to be composed of material that was blasted out of the Imbrium basin 3.9 billion years ago. Search this region to look for features that are radial to Mare Imbrium. They are further evidence of sculpting that resulted from the creation of the Imbrium basin.

Rima Ariadaeus: [NE/J11] The best place to see rilles on the Moon is in the area just west of Tranquillity. Here you will find a remarkably varied collection—to wit, Ariadaeus, Hyginus (two of the best-known rilles on the Moon) and Triesnecker. We'll start with Rima Ariadaeus tonight. The other two may still be hidden behind the terminator.

   When the terminator is close, Rima Ariadaeus is an enjoyable target even for small telescopes. It is a classic example of a **graben**, an elongated depression between two parallel fault lines where the ground in

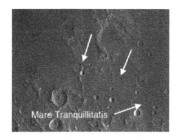

There is an astonishing *Apollo 10* photo of the Ariadaeus rille at *www.skyimage.com.* Click on Search, type in "Ariadaeus," then click on the image twice to enlarge it.

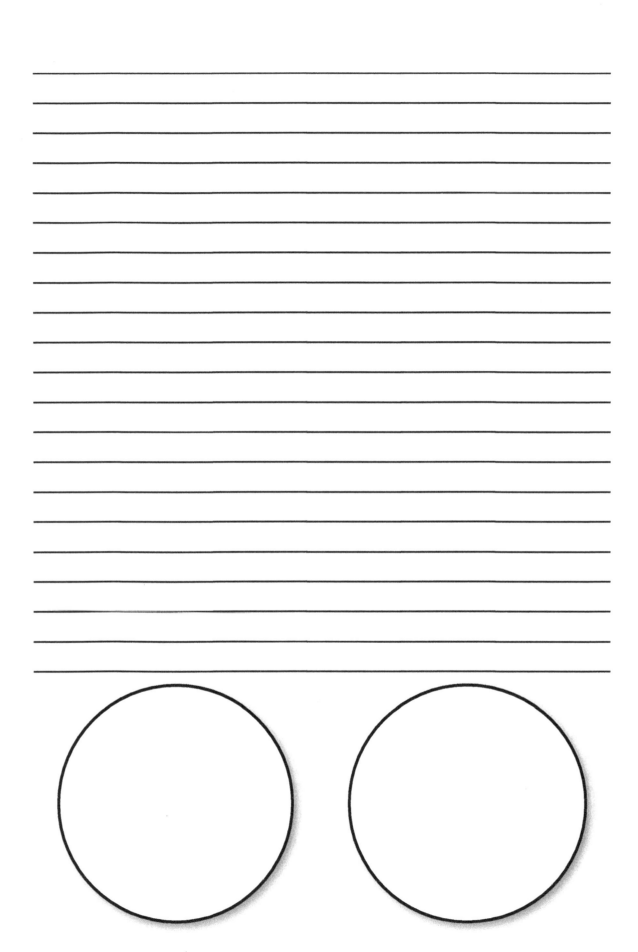

between has fallen away. If you have at least a 4" telescope with good optics and steady seeing, you will just be able to make out that the fault lines have pulled apart and the ground in between has sunk. (This is a challenge; Ariadaeus is a shade over two arc-seconds wide.) The rille appears to be broken in a few places, indicating that the lunar terrain has shifted since it was created, and there is a shunt on its western end connecting it to Rima Hyginus.

Manilius: [NE/H10] Conspicuously located just east of Mare Vaporum, although Manilius is only 24 miles in diameter, it is a prominent Tycho-class crater with terraces and central peaks.

Rima Hyginus: [NE/J10] At the west end of the Ariadaeus rille there is a narrow diagonal shunt that connects Ariadaeus to Rima Hyginus. This new rille parallels Rima Ariadaeus for about 20 miles, then continues west until it encounters the small 6-mile crater Hyginus. At that precise point it changes direction and veers northward toward Mare Vaporum. 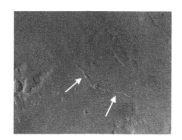 The fact that Hyginus crater is located precisely at the pivot point is a curiosity. Can this just be coincidence?

Rima Hyginus is 2.5 miles wide and is easily seen in very small telescopes. It is really made up of a line of linked craters which are best seen just northwest of the crater Hyginus. With good optics and steady seeing you might be able to make some of these out even with a three-inch scope. Wood suggests that these are actually rimless collapse pits of internal origin and that the crater Hyginus (also rimless) might be one of their number. Can you see any of the individual craters, or does Rima Hyginus just look like a linear feature?

Theophilus, Cyrillus, Catharina: [Repeated from Day 5—SE/L12] This is the most imposing trio of craters on the Moon. They are located just west of Mare Nectaris and have their own distinct personalities.

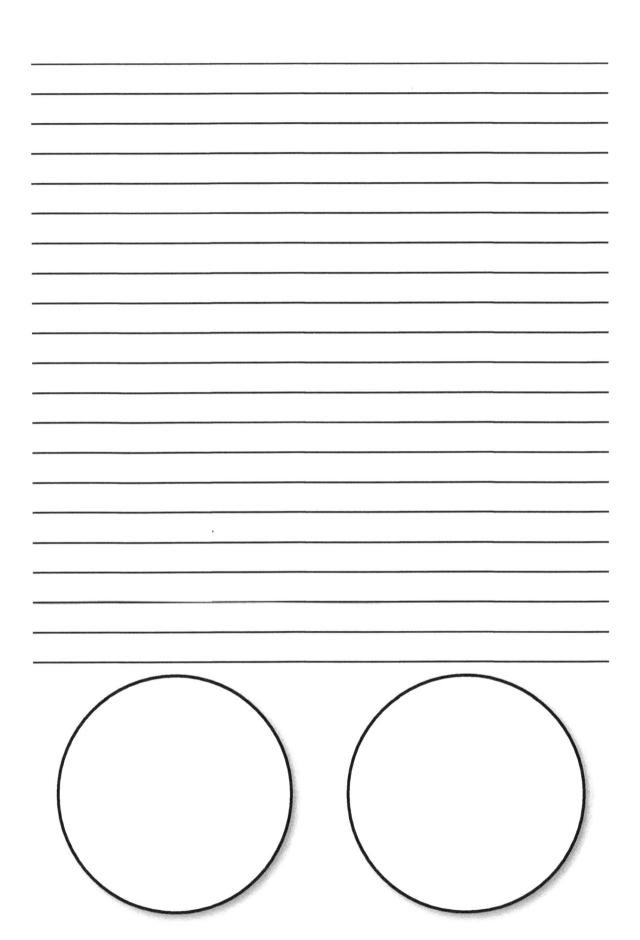

Theophilus is a spectacular formation with all of the attendant complexities of a Tycho-class crater: terraced walls, a flat floor, and magnificent central mountain peaks. It is 60 miles in diameter, and the drop from the highest mountains on the rim to the floor below is a breathtaking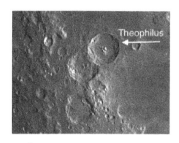
2.7 miles! Observers have reported that the shape of the central mountain seems to change as the lunation progresses. If you observed this crater last night, see if you can notice any differences in the shape of the central mountain.

Notice how the floor of Theophilus is much smoother than the floors of Cyrillus and Catharina. When the impact occurred that produced Theophilus, much of the material that was excavated shot straight up. When it returned (in the form of molten rocks and mountain-sized boulders), it splashed, spread out, and then resurfaced the floor with a smooth veneer.

> "Slosh" is such a gentle term. It is commonly used to describe the Theophilus event, but it reminds us only of the last time we carelessly handled a cup of coffee. Now imagine yourself as an astronaut standing on the rim of Theophilus whose entire floor, nearly three miles below, is bubbling with hot lava. Suddenly huge sections of the far wall, 60 miles away, detach themselves and slam into the lake, raising a tidal wave of lava so high that it will crash over the cliff you are standing on and flood the plains to the north for another 60 miles. "Slosh" is probably not the first word that would come to mind.

There is also **impact melt** around the crater exterior that can be easily seen with backyard telescopes. Take advantage of this, as there are not many places on the Moon where you can see such a thing. Most of this exterior impact melt occurs to the north of the crater and flows into *Sinus Asperitatis*. Charles Wood points out that this is because the south rim is higher. Shortly after impact, the terraces collapsed into the lake of molten rock below. This sent tidal waves of hot lava racing toward the opposite side. Because the north rim is lower, the material slammed into the wall, sloshed over the rim and pooled on the north side as impact melt.

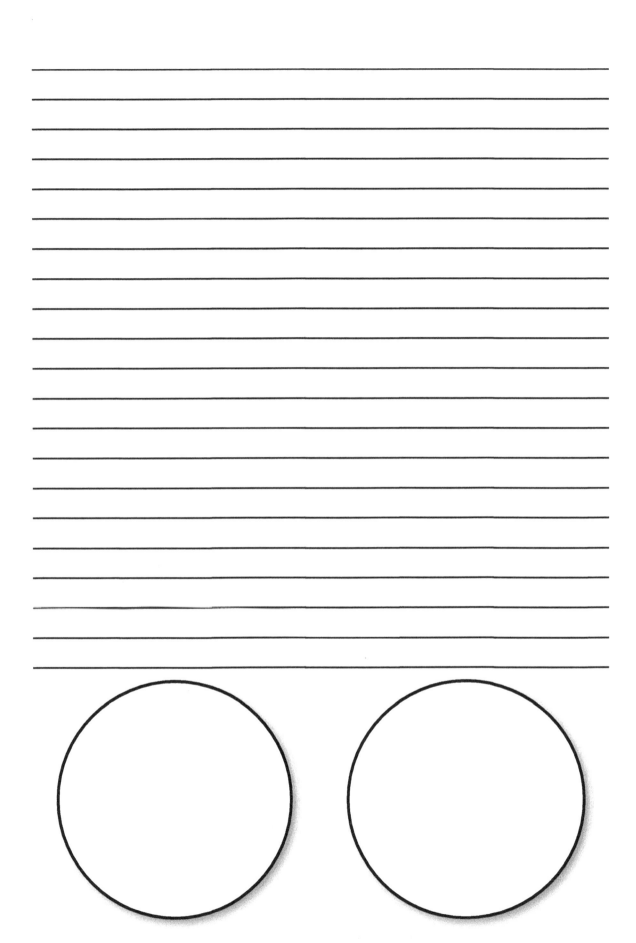

Can you figure out the comparative ages of the three craters?[17]

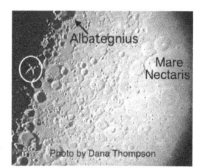

Photo by Dana Thompson

Lunar X: [SE/M10] Around 6 days 22 hours (depending on libration—you have to get this pretty exact, it's a narrow window) as the terminator crosses Blanchinus, the Sun will light up the mountain peaks immediately to the west of the crater and you will see a brilliantly lit "X" at the intersection of the rims of Blanchinus, La Caille, and Purbach. Look for it when the **terminator** is between 2° east and 1° west. Once it has formed, the image will last only for about three hours. The formation is also known as the Purbach Cross and the Werner X. (Because it is not an officially recognized object, you will not find it listed on the *Field Map*.)

Maurolycus: [SE/P11] Let us venture briefly into a region where angels fear to tread, the lunar Highlands. Plunge in and look for the crater Maurolycus. Although the area looks confusing, Maurolycus will be the largest and most conspicuous crater in this sector. It is a breathtaking sight under an early morning Sun and should not be missed. Maurolycus displays a rich diversity of different types of features. How many can you see? The central mountain peaks are so tall that they are illuminated long before the Sun finds its way to the dark floor. Also notice how Maurolycus overlaps a smaller unnamed crater on its southern border. This flies in the face of the rule that says younger craters are always smaller.

---

[17] Theophilus is younger than Cyrillus because it intrudes upon the latter's rim. Catharina seems to be the oldest because there are five craters superimposed on it, and two elongated craters on its northeast rim point back toward Mare Imbrium, suggesting that Catharina is even older than Imbrium!

Stöfler: [SE/P10] While you are swimming through the confusion of the Southern Highlands, try to find the crater Stöfler—it's a treasure! (If you located Maurolycus above, then Stöfler is located immediately to its west.) There are three large craters lined up on the same latitude (Orontius, Stöfler, and Maurolycus) that reward examination.

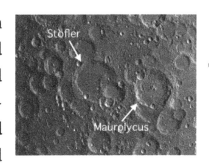

Some craters manifestly conform to the standard expectations—larger craters are older than smaller, younger craters intrude upon their elders. Stöfler is one of the best examples of this process. There is quite an impressive train wreck of craters on its southeast rim, all conforming to the rules—or almost all. Puzzle out the sequence for yourself before continuing with the next paragraph, and see if you can find the one exception.

Start with the smallest, youngest, and topmost crater on the southern rim of the "train wreck," Faraday C. This crater substantially intrudes upon Faraday P to its immediate west, which lies atop the southwest rim of Faraday, the largest and most conspicuous intruder of Stöfler. (But can you see that Faraday actually cuts into an older ruined crater on Stöfler's floor? It's such a short fragment that it's not possible to gauge its size.) If you look carefully, you can make out that Stöfler encroaches onto a smaller crater to its immediate southwest, which would make Stöfler both younger and larger. What do you think?

Day 7 (T=0°)

Days 7 and 8 offer so much to see and do that you will have to just keep coming back every month to take it all in. The precise moment of second quarter occurs when the terminator runs exactly down the center of the Moon's disk, the moment of true dichotomy.

Aristillus/Autolycus: [NE/F10] Aristillus is a well-defined complex crater, 34 miles in diameter, with a substantial ejecta blanket, terraces, and a central collection of mountain peaks. How many can you count? An examination of the floors of Aristillus and its close neighbor to the south, Autolycus, will indicate

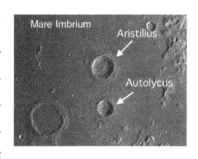

that they formed after the lava flows that filled the Imbrium basin. If you are favored by good lighting, immediately to the north of Aristillus you will be able to make out the outlines of an unnamed **ghost crater** which was almost entirely submerged beneath the lava flows. Notice how ejected material from the Aristillus impact covers the southern portion of this spectral image. Can you make out an unusual dark band that travels up the northeast inner slope and disappears over the rim? (See **banded craters** in the *Glossary*.) When we get closer to Full Moon you will notice that Aristillus is at the center of a ray system (which means that it is less than a billion years old—a mere youngster in lunar terms!).

Linné: [Repeated from Day 6—NE/G11] Linné is a simple, relatively young crater with an interesting history. It is 1.5 miles in diameter (only about 1.3 arc-seconds at the average distance of the Moon), which makes it about twice the size of **Meteor Crater**

Splash rays are pummeled out of existence after a billion years or so of micrometeorite bombard-ment and weathering by the solar wind.

in Arizona. Linné is surrounded by very light-colored material, and, because its appearance changes so much with different angles of illumination, this was once taken as evidence that the Moon was not a totally dead place. In 1866 it was erroneously reported that Linné had vanished. The idea caught on and was cited as proof that the Moon was still geologically active. Observe Linné under different lighting angles and see if you can convince yourself (if you didn't know better) that Linné could disappear. Observe it over the next few days, then come back at Full Moon and compare.

Mare Vaporum: [Repeated from Day 6—NE/H10] Notice how there are finger-like projections extending from the back side of the Apennines into Mare Vaporum. It is not coincidental that these extensions point back to Mare Imbrium as they are part of the ejecta that was thrown out during the initial impact. (This also makes the Sea of Vapors considerably younger than Mare Imbrium.) Notice how the lava seas have flowed smoothly into the bays and fjords of the Apennine Mountains. This is a clear indication that the Apennines were in place long before the lava seas flowed into the Mare Vaporum depression.

Take a comparative look at Mare Vaporum and Sinus Medii. It should be obvious which is younger. What do you think?[18]

Rima Ariadaeus: [Repeated from Day 6—NE/J11] The best place to see rilles on the Moon is in the area just west of Tranquillity. Here you will find a remarkably varied collection—to wit, Ariadaeus, Hyginus (two of the best-known rilles on the Moon) and Triesnecker.

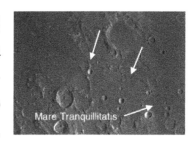
Mare Tranquillitatis

Rima Ariadaeus started to come into view last night. All three should be visible tonight.

---

[18] The Sea of Vapors is younger—the simple reason being that its floors are smoother. Over a longer time the floor of Vapors would have accumulated more meteor impacts.

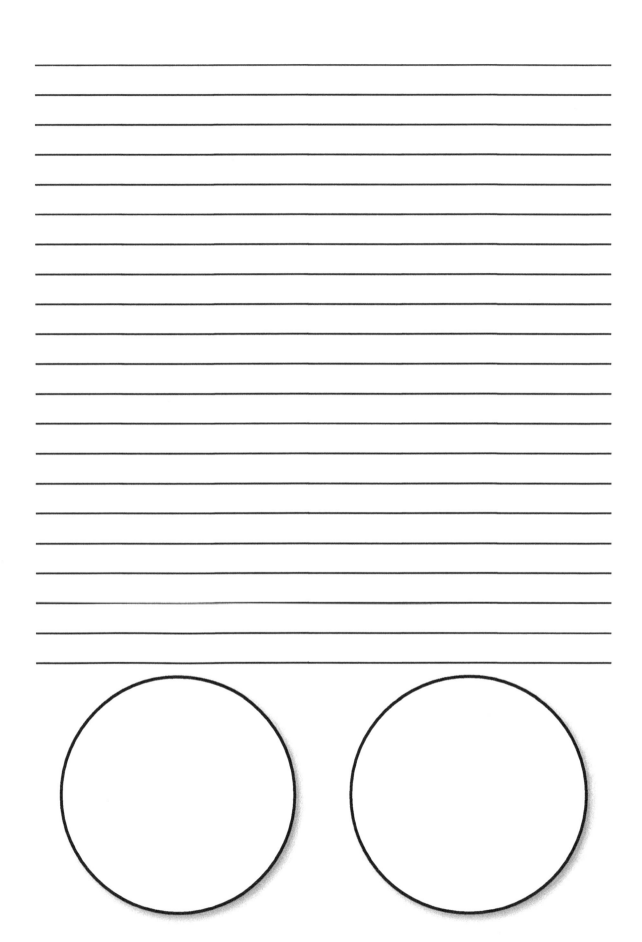

When the terminator is close, Rima Ariadaeus is an enjoyable target even for small telescopes. It is a classic example of a **graben**, an elongated depression between two parallel fault lines where the ground in between has fallen away.[19] If you have at least a 4" telescope with good optics and steady seeing you will just be able to make out that the fault lines have pulled apart and the ground in between has sunk. (This is a challenge; Ariadaeus is a shade over two arc-seconds wide.) The rille appears to be broken in a few places, indicating that the lunar terrain has shifted since it was created, and there is a shunt on its western end connecting it to Rima Hyginus.

Triesnecker: [NE/J10] This crater is located in Sinus Medii (*Central Bay*), the southern portion of which is "ground zero" on the Moon (latitude 0°, longitude 0°). Triesnecker is a good illustration of what a complex crater looks like. It has a central peak, terraces, and unusually large amounts of slump material that has separated from the western rim and fallen onto the floor. This would have been a spectacular landslide, creating a wave of material that slammed all the way to the central mountain nearly 6 miles away! You can see that significant slumping has occurred on the east rim also.

Rimae Triesnecker: [NE/J10] What a great place to poke around with your telescope! This is such a complex system of rilles that it looks like a railway switchyard! Which do you think came first, the crater or the rilles?[20]

The width of the rilles measures between one-half mile and one mile. The largest rilles can be seen in a three-inch refractor, but the whole system requires larger apertures and good seeing. There are at least nine

---

[19] There is an astonishing *Apollo 10* photo of the Ariadaeus rille at *www.skyimage.com*. Click on Search, type in "Ariadaeus," then click on the image twice to enlarge it.

[20] There is a rille approaching Triesnecker's northeast rim that looks like it has been interrupted by the crater, suggesting that the rilles were there first.

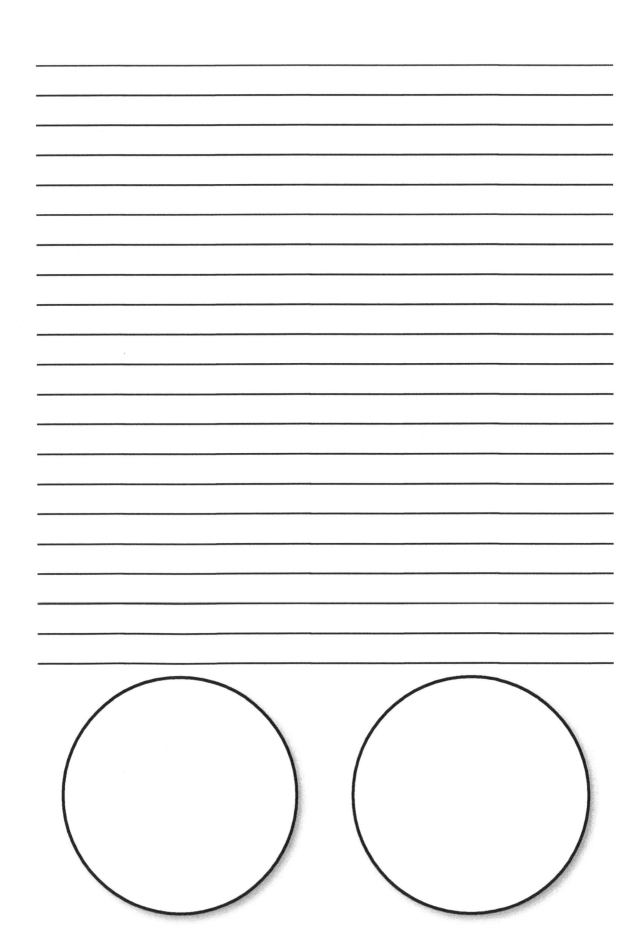

rilles crisscrossing each other. Make a sketch of how many you can see, then come back later and try to improve on it.

Scientists are not sure how the Triesnecker rilles developed. Their origin still remains a mystery, but the consensus is they are not **grabens** (as the above Ariadaeus rille is). Enjoy them as one of the Moon's many enigmas.

Rima Hyginus: [Repeated from Day 6—NE/J10] At the west end of the Ariadaeus rille there is a narrow diagonal shunt that connects Ariadaeus to Rima Hyginus. This new rille parallels Rima Ariadaeus for about 20 miles, then continues west until it encoun-  ters the small 6-mile crater Hyginus. At that precise point it changes direction and veers northward toward Mare Vaporum. The fact that Hyginus crater is located at the pivot point is a curiosity. Can this just be coincidence?

Rima Hyginus is 2.5 miles wide and is easily seen in very small telescopes. It is really made up of a line of linked craters which are best seen just northwest of the crater Hyginus. With good optics and steady seeing you might be able to make some of these out even with a three-inch scope. Wood suggests that these are actually rimless collapse pits of internal origin, and that the crater Hyginus (also rimless) might be one of their number. Can you see any of the individual craters, or does Rima Hyginus just look like a linear feature?

Plato:† [NW/D9] Wait until the terminator is a little to the west of Plato (toward the end of Day 7 or be- ginning of Day 8, depending on libration) and you will witness one of the Moon's loveliest sights. At such a time, the early morning Sun will be filtering through 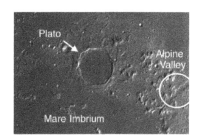 the mountain peaks and casting long spire-like shadows on Plato's floor. Within a short time it will look like the skyline of an entire city has been outlined on the interior plains of Plato. The process begins quite magically as small areas on

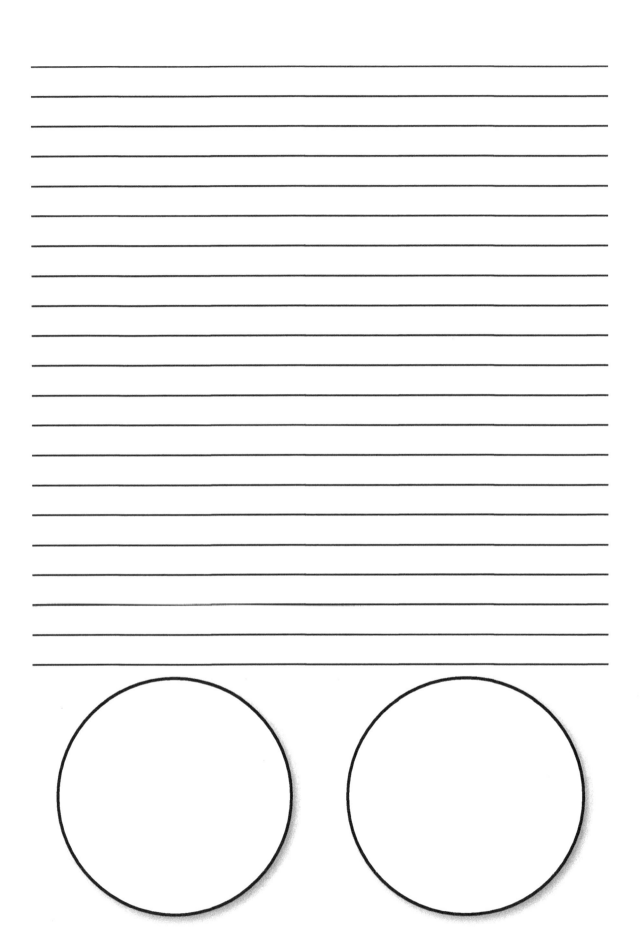

Plato's floor start to glow eerily. If you're not prepared for it, you'll be mystified by what is happening, but within a short time the outline of the eastern rim peaks will take shape and become apparent. If you're lucky enough to catch this process at the beginning, come back every 15 minutes or so to watch the scene unfold.

There are a few instances where craters are seemingly complex, such as Plato and Archimedes (below), but they are lacking the requisite central peaks. So what happened? The peaks are still there; they are actually 1.2 miles high, but they've been entirely buried by torrential lava flows! Plato's original floor is actually 1.5 miles deeper than it appears here.

Alpine Valley: [NE/E10] This is one of the Moon's major attractions. The valley is 120 miles long and 6 miles wide. When the Imbrium basin was formed 3.9 billion years ago, the resulting stresses produced two parallel fault lines in this area of the lunar Alps. The lines pulled apart and the terrain in between dropped

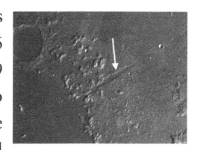

away to produce this lovely valley (technically called a **graben**). Try to catch it right after sunrise as the photogenic effect diminishes with a higher Sun angle.

There is a challenging object running straight down the middle of the Alpine Valley, and you really should persist until you have seen it. A stream of hot lava had cut a tiny rille meandering down its middle. The rille is visible through a 5" refractor (provided that you have excellent optics and great seeing). An 8-inch telescope will increase your chances considerably.

Mons Pico: [NW/E9] At the end of Day 7 and the beginning of Day 8, when the terminator has just cleared Plato, the redundantly named Mount Pico[21] and its little brother Pico β, about 25 miles to its south

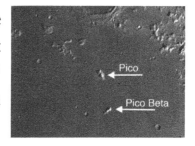

---

[21] "Pico" is Spanish for *peak*.

are striking, statuesque features which stand sentinel on the lava plains of Mare Imbrium. The "Brothers Pico" are surviving fragments of what was at one time the magnificent inner ring of the Imbrium basin. At this time Pico and Pico β will be casting long shadows that fall across the nearby **wrinkle ridges**. Mount Pico towers an impressive 1.5 miles over the plains below!

Mons Piton: [NE/E9] Mount Piton is nearly as tall as Mount Pico but has an extra treat: a meteor landed smack on top of its summit and left a tiny crater! Glimpsing the crater requires a night of steady seeing and good optics.

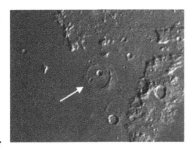

Cassini: [NE/E10] Can you tell by looking at Cassini that it was created on the Imbrium floor *before* the lavas started to flow? The floor of Cassini appears to be at sea level with the rest of Imbrium (this would not be possible if Cassini were created *after* the lava flows), and aside from a few obvious disturbances, much of it is quite smooth. Cassini's size (35 mi.) and the width and complexity of its ramparts suggest that its basin should have substantial depth and central mountain peaks, but it is quite shallow.

Take a close look at Cassini under high magnification. The two tiny bumps (you might see three) just to the southwest of the largest internal crater give you a clue about the timing of the impact. Cassini was at one time quite deep with central mountains appropriate to its size. The post-Imbrium lavas that flooded the crater rose so high that all that is left of the once impressive central mountain peaks are these little bumps.

The floor of Cassini is covered with features, some of which can be easily seen with a small telescope, but

Considering that Cassini is fairly conspicuous, it is curious that none of the early maps mentioned it until 1692 when Giovanni Cassini discovered the crater and named it after himself (a benefit that astronomers are allowed to bestow upon themselves when they make a discovery).

others are quite delicate and require larger apertures and good seeing. Make a rough sketch of what you see and come back later to fill in more details. You will have no trouble with the two larger internal craters, Cassini A (9 mi.) and Cassini B (6 mi.). Can you see how Cassini A is shaped like a teardrop pointing toward the northeast? The teardrop shape was the result either of a closely spaced double impact or of an oblique impact.

Notice how Cassini's **glacis**, a wreath-like outer rim that would normally extend out farther, has been partially covered by the flow of Imbrium lavas. Cassini and Archimedes (below) share a similar history. Compare them closely to see what characteristics they have in common.

Archimedes:† [NW/G9] This is a prominent 50-mile crater with terraces and a surprisingly smooth floor. At sunrise Archimedes is a magnificent sight with shadow spires stretching across its internal plains. A similar image is reproduced on Plato's smooth, dark chocolate floor [NW/D9] with even greater effect. (You may have 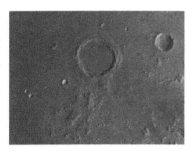 to wait until tomorrow night to see this.) Craters the size of Archimedes should have a hefty set of mountain peaks at their center. The peaks are actually there, but they have been completely covered by lava, now two miles deep, that flowed up through fractures in the floor. Because the lava had the viscosity of hot maple syrup, the floors appear nearly as smooth as an ice rink. As a result, there has been an informal competition over the years to see how many small impact craters can be made out on the floor. Make a quick drawing of the craterlets that you see, and come back later to try to improve on the count.

Compare Archimedes with its neighbors Aristillus and Autolycus [F10]. An examination of their rough floors will indicate that these two craters were formed *after* the Imbrium lava flows. Notice how the lavas have risen around Archimedes and partially bury its surrounding ejecta blanket.

Immediately south of Archimedes is a light-hued mountainous terrain. This feature is a curiosity in that it is the only part of the Imbrium basin that had not been inundated by lava flows. Wood posits an interesting theory for this: He calls our attention to a large mass of material on the front side of the Apennines [G9-10] and to some long, narrow arcuate ridges on either side of this mass that poke up through the Imbrium lavas and hug the mountain range. He suggests that these formations are the tops of enormous terrace walls that slumped down onto the basin floor with such energy that this region was uplifted as a grand plateau and was protected from inundation by later lava flows.

Both Archimedes and Cassini (above) share a similar history. Compare them closely to see what characteristics they have in common.

Rima Hadley:† [NE/G10] This feature formed as lava from a nearby volcanic vent flowed onto the plains of Palus Putredinis.[22] The lava cut a deep channel that is wide enough to be seen today in amateur telescopes. It is 75 miles long, one mile wide, and 1,300 feet deep. The sickle-shaped volcanic vent from which the lava spewed can be briefly glimpsed each month. It lies perpendicular to the southwest end of the rille. (Look for it when the terminator is around 1° east.)

Astronauts made important discoveries at Hadley Rille. Scientists wanted to get better information on the depth of the Imbrium basin and its age. Hadley Rille afforded the Apollo 15 astronauts an opportunity to examine a deep cross section of the basin. They brought back rock samples that proved that the Apennines were formed as a direct result of the impact that blasted out Mare Imbrium 3.9 billion years ago.

The best time to view Hadley Rille is when the terminator cuts through the nearby plains of Palus Putredinis at 0.4° E. Its width of only one mile would subtend an angle of less than an arc-second, but lines are easier to see than points.

---

[22] Which may be roughly translated as "the Marsh of Great Stinkiness." (What a vacation spot!)

You would normally need a 5-inch telescope and good conditions to see Hadley Rille. What size instrument can you see it with?

Montes Apenninus: [NW/H9-G10] The Apennine Mountain Range is the most spectacular feature on the Moon and was formed when the Imbrium basin was blasted out nearly four billion years ago. Mountain ranges on the Earth take millions of years to form. The magnificent ranges that surround Mare Imbrium were 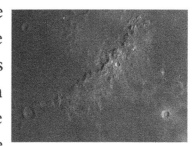 created in a matter of minutes! They resulted from the shock waves that exploded out from the original Imbrium impact. The Apennines stretch out over 370 miles and include more than 3,000 peaks. The highest peak in this range is Mons Huygens [NW/G9] which stretches, from its base to its top, to an incredible 18,000 feet!

Back off and scan the whole area for telltale formations that seem to radiate from the center of Imbrium (don't forget to check the back side of the Apennines). These radial features resulted from debris that was blown out from the original impact.

Stadius: [NW/H8] Located just southwest of Eratosthenes, Stadius is so heavily flooded that it is almost a **ghost crater**; however, it does retain some incomplete low walls that just barely break through the surface of the lava plain, qualifying it as a ruined crater rather than just circular **wrinkle ridges**.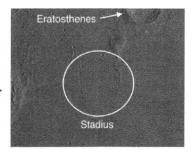

There is an unnamed but striking **catena** (crater chain) extending north-northwest from Stadius up toward the shore of Imbrium. These are secondary craters resulting from the Copernicus impact (which may not be seen until tomorrow night). Can you make out the individual craters, or do they blend together as a rille-like feature?

Lunar City: [NW/J9] Once upon a time there was a famous lunar observer and selenographer[23] by the name of Baron von Gruithuisen (GROOT.hoo.zen). The Baron was famous for two things: 1) He was a good observer and selenographer (three lunar formations are named after him), and 2) He had a wild and fanciful imagination. He wrote an entire book detailing his discovery of what he believed to be the ruins of a magnificent lunar city, complete with "colossal buildings and gigantic ramparts" and other evidence of "Moon-dwellers." In spite of a strong penchant for science, he tended to live in a land of make-believe.

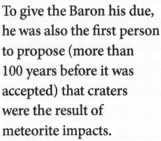

To give the Baron his due, he was also the first person to propose (more than 100 years before it was accepted) that craters were the result of meteorite impacts.

Tonight you have an opportunity to visit the baron's lunar city. Take a deep breath, make yourself temporarily credulous, throw your telescope (and your mind) a little out of focus, and scan the mountain region about 60 miles north of the ruined crater Schröter (Schröter is 20 miles in diameter). The southern boundary of the lunar city begins at the crater Schröter W and continues north for a short distance. To view the city, the terminator must be very close.

Hipparchus:† [SE/K10] a large, degraded crater. Look for evidence of Imbrium sculpting on its walls and in the environs.

Albategnius: [SE/L10] Albategnius is a delight! It is an 85-mile complex crater located just east of the Ptolemaeus trio (see below) in the central Highlands. Sunrise over Albategnius is a lovely sight, as the jagged peaks on the eastern rim will cast many shadow spires on the floor. This is a good place to observe the

---

[23] Selenography: the study of the physical features of the Moon.

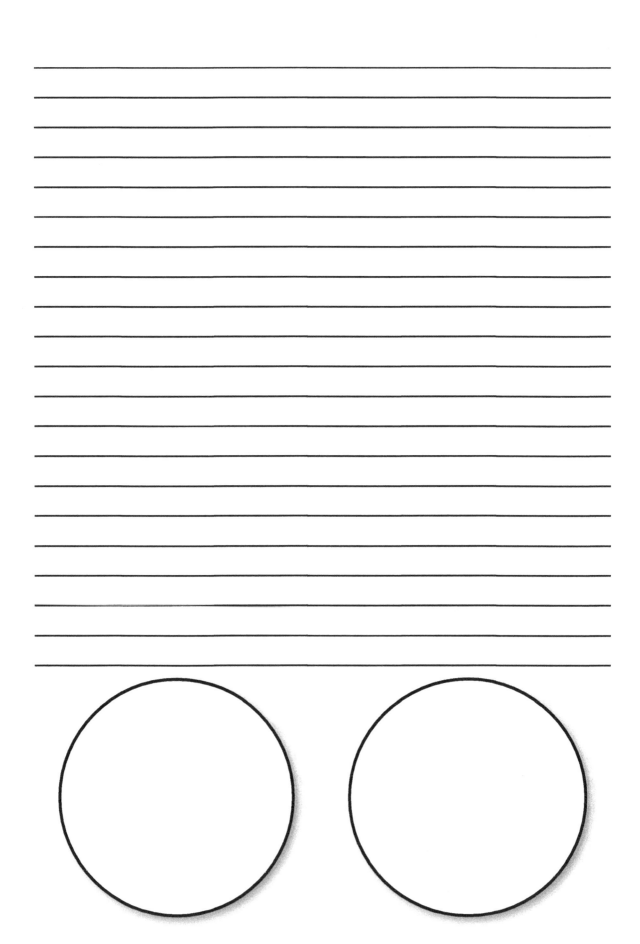

standard sequence of crater formation. Look for hints that alert you to the **D** comparative ages of the different craters. On its southwest rim, Albategnius **A** is overlapped by Klein (27 mi.) which in turn is intruded upon by Klein A (± 5 **Y** mi.) on its NE rim. Both Albategnius and Klein have **central peaks**, but notice how Albat's central mountain seems to have been pushed off center and, astonishingly, **7** a meteorite has landed with precise accuracy on the very tip of its highest peak, leaving a tiny craterlet as a memento! Because the craterlet is only 1 mile in diameter, it will seriously test your optics, the seeing conditions, and your experience!

Immediately east of Albategnius, touching its rim, you can see further evidence of Imbrium **sculpting**, verifying that Albategnius was in place before the impact that excavated Mare Imbrium.

Ptolemaeus, Alphonsus, Arzachel: [SW/K-L9] (These may not be revealed until halfway through Day 7, or wait until tomorrow night.) This is the second group of favorite show-stopping trios on the Moon (the first being Theophilus, Cyrillus, and Catharina which you saw on Day 5). Both trios will richly reward close

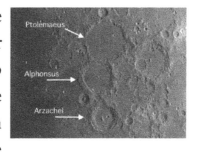

examination. Debris from the Imbrium impact has carved long valleys into the area immediately surrounding these craters. Examine the neighborhood when the terminator is close. (Don't overlook the opportunity to revisit around Day 22 when the Sun is setting over these features.)

Ptolemaeus:† [SW/K9] At 95 miles in diameter, Ptolemaeus is so large that Copernicus, "the Monarch of the Moon" would easily fit inside its walls with room to spare. It has a relatively smooth floor. Wood suggests that material thrown out from the Imbrium impact landed inside Ptolemaeus, and because this debris was

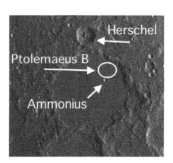

still in a molten state, it spread out and ponded within the crater walls. By rights, Ptolemaeus should have an impressive central mountain complex (compare the much smaller *Herschel* immediately to its north) so the "ponding" was pretty substantial.

> If you were an astronaut standing in the middle of Ptolemaeus, you'd think you were in Kansas. The surrounding mountains would lie below the horizon!

Ptolemaeus departs somewhat from the standard circularity of craters. With only a slight twist of the imagination, it can be made to look like a perfect hexagon with more or less straight sides. Catch it under an early morning Sun and you will be able to see the ghost images of several subsurface craters trying to percolate through to the top. They resemble very shallow saucers. The most obvious of these, *Ptolemaeus B*, just touches the north rim of the 6-mile crater *Ptolemaeus A* (aka *Ammonius*) located in the northeast quadrant of Ptolemaeus. There are also several craterlets from 0.5 to 3 miles that will test your optics and the seeing conditions. Try to make out the unnamed crater chain extending between the northeast rim and the 12-mile crater Müller. This crater chain (or **catena**) is not radial to Mare Imbrium, so it is possibly the result of a comet that had been ripped into a series of smaller parts. They then impacted on the Moon in machine-gun fashion (for comparison see *Catena Davy* just on the west side of Ptolemaeus on Day 8).

Both to the north and west of Ptolemaeus you will see long parallel valleys that have been cut out by boulders and debris flying out from the Imbrium impact. Notice how they all point directly back, with accusing fingers, to their explosive place of origin. This is lunar **sculpting** at its best.

Alphonsus: [SW/L9] Examine the adjoining rims of Ptolemaeus and Alphonsus. Which crater do you think appeared first?[24] Alphonsus is one of the more

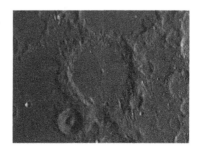

---

[24] Can you see that the northern rim of Alphonsus intrudes slightly into Ptolemaeus, making Alphonsus the younger crater?

interesting craters on the Moon. It not only has a central peak and a floor that displays rilles and small craters, some of the craterlets have enigmatic dark halos around them. These halos are the result of a little-known but fascinating volcanic activity called explosive pyroclastic eruptions. As magma is spewing out from volcanic vents, sometimes gases that are trapped within will suddenly expand and cause the molten rocks to explode in a shower of tiny dark glass beads. The result is that the area surrounding the source vent is covered by a dark halo of *pyroclastic deposits*. Alphonsus is the best place on the Moon for you to see the results of this phenomenon through backyard telescopes. Three of the most conspicuous halos are located close to the east rim and are connected by a thin rille.

> In 1965, Ranger 9 crashed onto the floor of Alphonsus. Before its suicidal impact, it captured images which revealed that the Alphonsus rilles were actually chains of craterlets that have run together.

D A Y 7

Before you leave Alphonsus, notice how debris from the Imbrium impact has cut valleys completely through the southeastern rim! The low mountain ridge cutting through the center of Alphonsus is also thought to be ejecta from the Imbrium impact.

Arzachel: [SW/L9] This is the youngest crater of the three and has much to offer even for observers with small telescopes. Arzachel is a complex crater with terraces, rilles, hills, craterlets, and a slightly off-center "central" mountain which rises 4,900 ft. from the floor! Arzachel has two challenging rim craterlets. The easiest 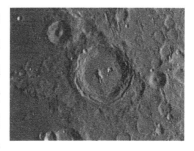 is on its northwest rim. If you can find that, then look carefully at the most prominent craterlet, Arzachel A, just to the east of the central mountain. Can you see that it has a tiny crater superimposed on its southwest rim? Enormous landslides on Arzachel were so severe that they actually opened up two valleys inside its southwest and southeast rims.

Arzachel A is nearly 6 miles in diameter, but there are a few smaller ones. Do a quick sketch of what you can see, then come back later and try to add to it.

Alpetragius: [SW/L9] Now we come to a crater that's just plain cute! Under the right lighting, Alpetragius (not to be confused with *Albategnius* above) looks remarkably like an oversized ostrich egg sitting incongruously in a smaller bird's nest. This is an unusual crater because even the largest central mountain peaks

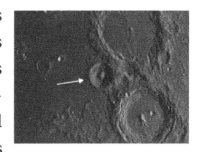

rarely take up more than one-third of the crater floor. Because of its large peak, Alpetragius is just bursting at the seams! So far nobody has come up with an adequate explanation of why this is so.

Thebit: [SW/M9] On the eastern shore of Mare Nubium, just to the west of the gap separating Arzachel from Purbach, lies Thebit—a textbook example of how to tell crater ages by their size and placement. Check out the series of craters overlapping Thebit and figure out the sequence of their appearance—this should be an

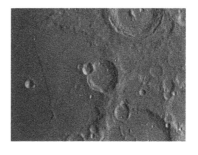

easy process by now. (Check the footnote if you're not sure.)[25] Can you make out the terracing on the east rim and the two tiny craters that have intruded on the north rim?

Lunar X: [Repeated from Day 6—SE/M10] Around 6 days 22 hours (depending on libration—it's a narrow window and you have to get this pretty exact) as the terminator crosses Blanchinus the Sun will light up the mountain peaks immediately to the west of the crater

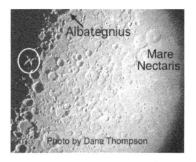

Albategnius

Mare Nectaris

Photo by Dana Thompson

---

[25] The large crater Thebit is overlapped by the younger and smaller crater Thebit A, which in turn is overlapped by the still younger and smaller Thebit L.

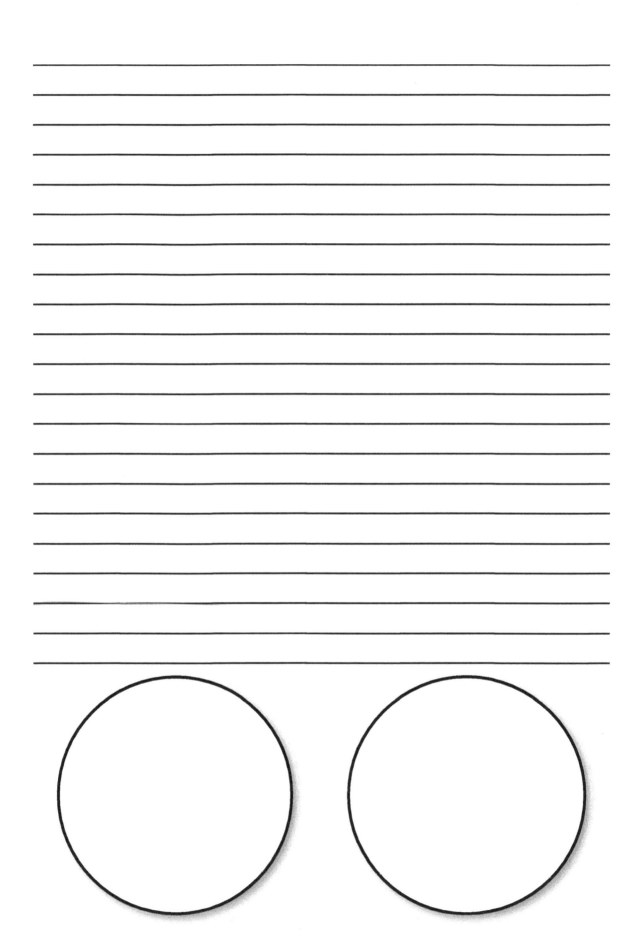

and you will see a brilliantly lit "X" at the intersection of the rims of Blanchinus, La Caille, and Purbach. Look for it when the **terminator** is between 2° east and 1° west. Once it has formed, the image will last only for about three hours. The formation is also known as the Purbach Cross and the Werner X.

Regiomontanus: [SW/M9] This is a crater that just exudes character and personality! It has a squashed, oblong shape that looks as if it's being squeezed out from a tight place between Purbach to its north and Deslandres toward the southwest (this is an important clue about which crater has seniority in the region.)[26]

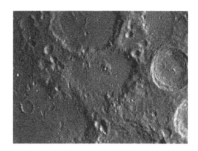

Despite its high state of disintegration, Regiomontanus retains many interesting features. It has a group of "central" mountains that seem to have wandered off-target (a result of the forces which turned it from a round crater into a squashed, oblong thing). There are eroded walls, complex ramparts, and a floor that is dotted with tiny craters. But there is something about its central mountain that is surprising. Look closely under high power and good seeing conditions and you might be able to see that a small meteor has impacted precisely on the tip of its highest peak and left a tiny 3½-mile craterlet in its place. Somebody must have been taking really good aim!

During much of the 20th century, there was a hot debate raging among scientists about whether craters were *exogenic* (resulting from impacts) or *endogenic* (caused by volcanic action). The crater on top of Regio's central peak looked so much like a volcano that the endogenic camp used it as evidence that their theory was correct. (The fact that thousands of craters *didn't* look like volcanoes didn't seem to trouble them very much.) As a result of the Apollo missions, the exogenic camp finally won out.

Clavius: [SW/Q8] If you catch the Moon at the end of Day 7 or early in Day 8 when the terminator is around 15° (i.e., it cuts right through Clavius), and if

---

[26] Regio is obviously older. Because it was in place first, when the other two interlopers arrived later they distorted its circular shape.

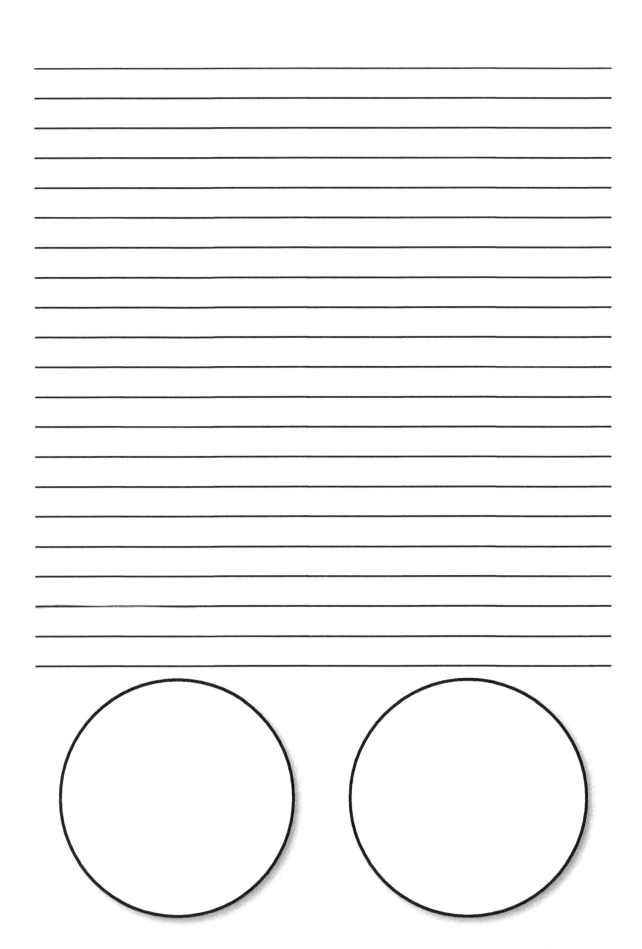

you have determined that you can see objects that are as small as 2 arc-minutes with the naked eye,[27] look at the Moon without benefit of telescope or binoculars and you might be able to see a small notch that has been chiseled out of the terminator in the southern portion of the Moon. This notch is the crater

Clavius. If you need to, double-check with binoculars then go back and see if you can detect it with your naked eyes. Come back tomorrow night to see Clavius in its full glory.

Sunrise over Clavius is something that you don't want to miss! The crater is so large (140 miles) that the curvature of the Moon pushes the floor's central regions into the sunlight first. As the day progresses the shadows will retreat to reveal a floor that is strewn with craterlets. There is a delightful arc of small craters, artistically and sequentially arranged in order of size, which begins at Rutherfurd, a 34-mile crater just inside the southeast rim, arcs northward and then diminishes toward the west. (You'll have to wait until tomorrow night to see the entire sequence.) While the Sun angle is low over Clavius, look for several ridges that extend like fingers northward from Rutherfurd. The origin of these ridges remains a mystery. Revisit Clavius often. You will always see something that you missed previously.

Deslandres: [SW/N9] (day.LAHN.druh) This is a large 145-mile crater located just inland from the southeast shore of Mare Nubium which, in spite of its partially ruined state, displays a number of interesting features: craterlets, crater chains, and hills which must be viewed under a low-angle Sun. Notice how the

---

[27] See **resolution** in the *Glossary* for a way to determine how small an object you can see with your naked eyes. This will probably vary between two and four arc-minutes.

crater Lexel, which has intruded on the southeast rim of Deslandres, seems to be a **subsidence** feature. Deslandres is in such a state of disrepair that it wasn't even recognized as a crater until well into the 20th century. If you had just run across Deslandres for the first time, would you have trouble identifying it as a crater (particularly when the Sun is higher and there is less contrast)?

Walther: [SW/N9] You will find this 87-mile crater adjoining Deslandres just to its east. Because it has some very complex ramparts, under an early morning Sun Walther is a strikingly beautiful object. It has an offset group of central mountains which has been impacted by several small craters.

Southern Highlands: There is a veritable blizzard of craters in a large region known as the Southern Highlands (centered around K-R10). Dive into them, at your own risk, around Days 7-8. A profitable exercise is to practice sorting craters out by age (Do they look fresh? Are the rims battered and worn down? Do craters overlap?) and by **morphology (simple? complex? basin?).**

> The Southern Highlands reminds me of an area of Utah called the *Maze* where I once hiked. Beginners are advised not to go into this area without a guide because within the first 15 minutes they will be so hopelessly lost they'll never find their way out.

**D
A
Y

7**

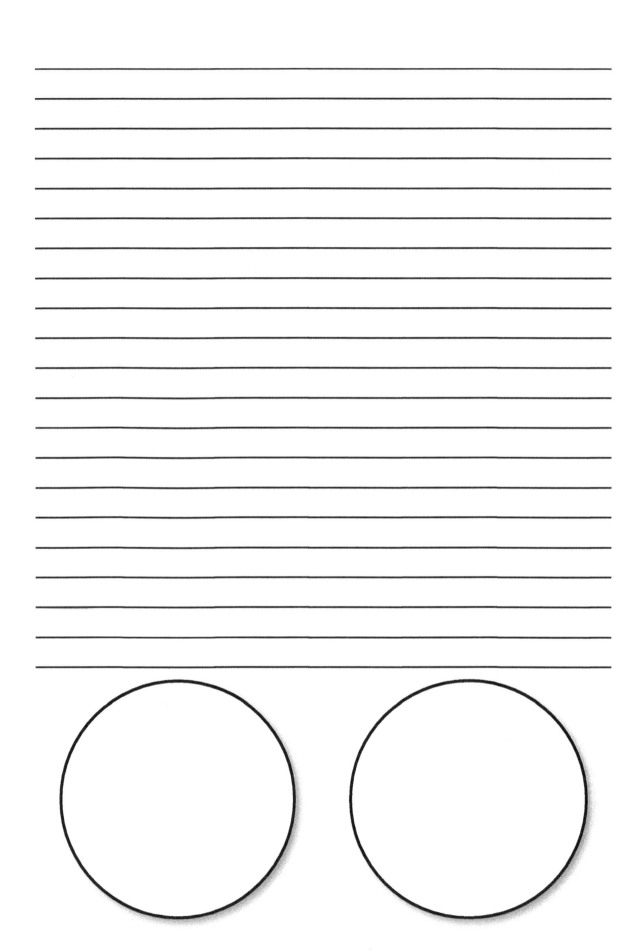

Day 8 (T=12° W)

The Moon has now entered its **gibbous** phase[28] and the terminator has become convex toward the west. Days 7 and 8 present the observer with a cornucopia of detail! At the beginning of Day 8 the terminator will have just cleared Plato, Eratoshtanes, and Tycho—a profitable time to observe all three craters. This is also a good opportunity to observe **wrinkle ridges** that you can see around the eastern side of Mare Imbrium running from Archimedes toward Plato. Many of these wrinkle ridges reveal the presence of hidden mountain ranges, now almost completely buried by lava flows, which formed the inner ring surrounding the impact zone when the Imbrium basin was formed.

Plato:† [Repeated from Day 7—NW/D9] Wait until the terminator is a little to the west of Plato (toward the end of Day 7 or beginning of Day 8, depending on libration) and you will witness one of the Moon's loveliest sights. At such a time, the early morning Sun will be filtering through the mountain peaks and

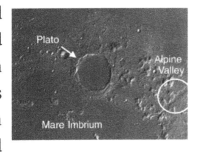

casting long spire-like shadows on Plato's floor. Within a short time it will look like the skyline of an entire city has been outlined on the interior plains of Plato. The process begins quite magically as small areas on Plato's floor start to glow eerily. If you're not prepared for it, you'll be mystified by what is happening, but within a short time the outline of the eastern rim peaks will take shape and become apparent. If you're lucky enough to catch this process at the beginning, come back every 15 minutes or so to watch the scene unfold.

---

[28] Gibbous: more than half but less than full.

There are a few instances where craters are seemingly complex, such as Plato and Archimedes (Day 7), but they are lacking the requisite central peaks. So what happened? The peaks are still there; they are actually 1.2 miles high, but they've been entirely buried by torrential lava flows! Plato's original floor is actually 1½ miles deeper than it appears here.

Johannes Hevelius, 17th century astronomer and founder of lunar topography, referred to Plato as "the Greater Black Lake."

DAY 8

There is a curious thing that happens to Plato as the Sun rises: the dark-chocolate floor appears to get even darker! This is an illusion. Photometric measurements have proven that the floor actually gets lighter, but it's hard to convince yourself of that. Come back over the next few nights and see what you think.

Plato's floor also presents us with an interesting challenge: There are several tiny craterlets that will test your instrument, your powers of observation, and the atmospheric seeing. There have occasionally been unofficial contests to detect the largest number of craters on Plato's floor. Although some amateurs have reported dozens, these reports may be specious. As a rule, consider yourself lucky if you can see four. Then come back and try to improve on that number.[29]

At one point in Plato's early history there was a dramatic shift of terrain when a large triangular massif, eight miles long, partially disconnected itself from the western rim and started to slide toward the floor. You can see this detached chunk even with small telescopes. And if you look around the rim a short distance to the north, you'll see there was a similar event.

Mare Imbrium: [±NW/F8] The Imbrium basin, whose eastern borders are just coming into view tonight, was created 3.9 billion years ago when an asteroid 60 miles

---

[29] The largest of the four is 1.3 miles in diameter, the smallest is 1 mile.

in diameter slammed into the Moon at 10 miles per second and blasted out a 720-mile-wide crater! It was at one time a spectacular multi-ring basin like Mare Orientale (see Day 13). Fortunately, segments of the original multi-ring features remain in the form of four stunning mountain ranges: the Alps, the Caucasus, the Apennines, and the Carpathians [±F10].

Unlike mountain ranges on the Earth, these ranges did not form by tectonic uplift; they were blasted into place by the impact that excavated Mare Imbrium (much like a billiard ball dropped into a tub of thick, viscous mud will leave a conspicuous circle of ridges around the point of impact). The Imbrium basin later filled up with lava that had the viscosity of hot maple syrup and therefore flowed very quickly, turning the mare basins into what were truly, for a time, liquid seas. (Early observers of the Moon weren't so far off base after all when they called these features "seas.")

Notice that the Alps have a smaller radius than the other three ranges. That's because they are part of the original *middle* ring. The Caucasus, Apennines, and Carpathians form the outer ring. The highest mountains in this outer ring rise more than 18,000 feet (nearly 3½ miles—providing the best skiing in the solar system!).

> There is an intriguing suggestion made by Charles Wood that the Caucasus Mountain Range has actually rotated from its original alignment with the Alps. Examine the placement of the Caucasus carefully and see if you can agree with his proposition.

Timocharis: [NW/G8] About three crater-diameters to the southwest of Archimedes (Day 7) is Timocharis, a **complex crater** that stands conspicuously isolated in the Imbrium Sea. It is 21 miles in diameter, 2 miles deep, and has a number of complexities that include a sharp rim, terraced walls, and an ejecta blanket. At one time in its past, Timocharis received a dead-center meteor impact that totally obliterated its central mountain!

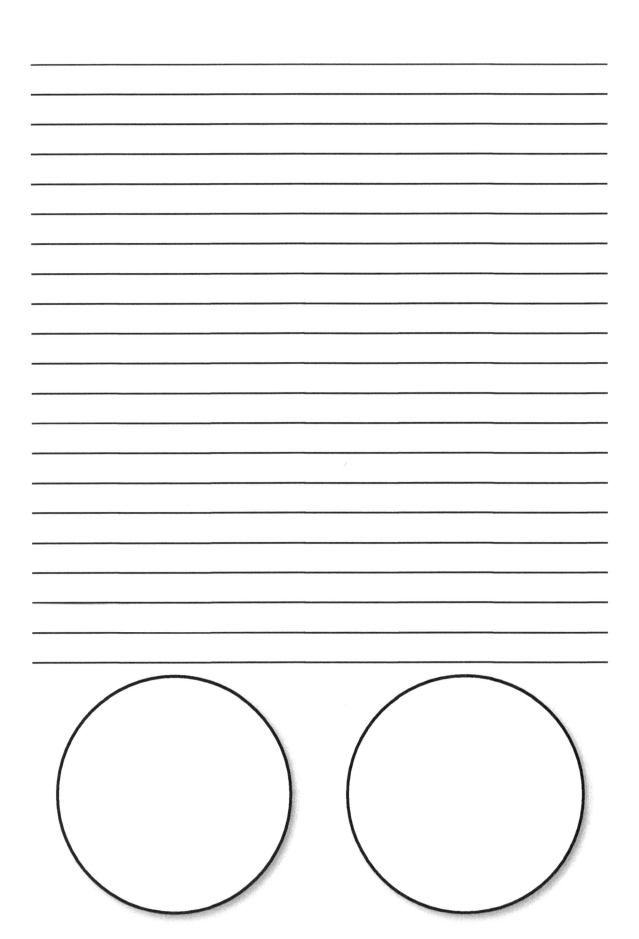

Montes Apenninus: [Repeated from Day 7—NW/H9-G10] The Apennine Mountain Range is the most spectacular feature on the Moon and was formed as a direct result of the impact that created the Imbrium basin nearly four billion years ago. Mountain ranges on the Earth take millions of years to form. The mag-nificent ranges that surround Mare Imbrium were created in a matter of minutes! They resulted from the shock waves that exploded out from the original Imbrium impact. The Apennines stretch out over 370 miles and include more than 3,000 peaks. The highest peak in this range is Mons Huygens [NW/G9] which stretches, from its base to its top, to an incredible 18,000 feet!

Back off and scan the whole area for telltale formations that seem to radiate from the center of Imbrium (don't forget to check the back side of the Apennines). These radial features resulted from debris that was blown out from the original impact.

Eratosthenes: [NW/H8] A large (36-mi.) complex crater with terraced walls, central peaks, and a thick ejecta blanket. Halfway between Eratosthenes and Copernicus you will find conspicuous lines of **secondary craters** arcing around Copernicus (or where you estimate Copernicus would be, since it is still beyond 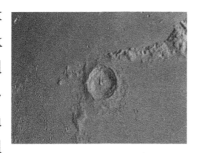the terminator tonight). These are some of the best secondary craters on the Moon.

Lalande A: [SW/K9] As craters increase in size their morphology progresses from **simple** through **complex** to **basin.** Simple craters start with rounded floors then progress to a flat floor resulting from a cascade of boulders that have rolled down the interior walls

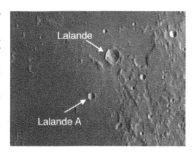

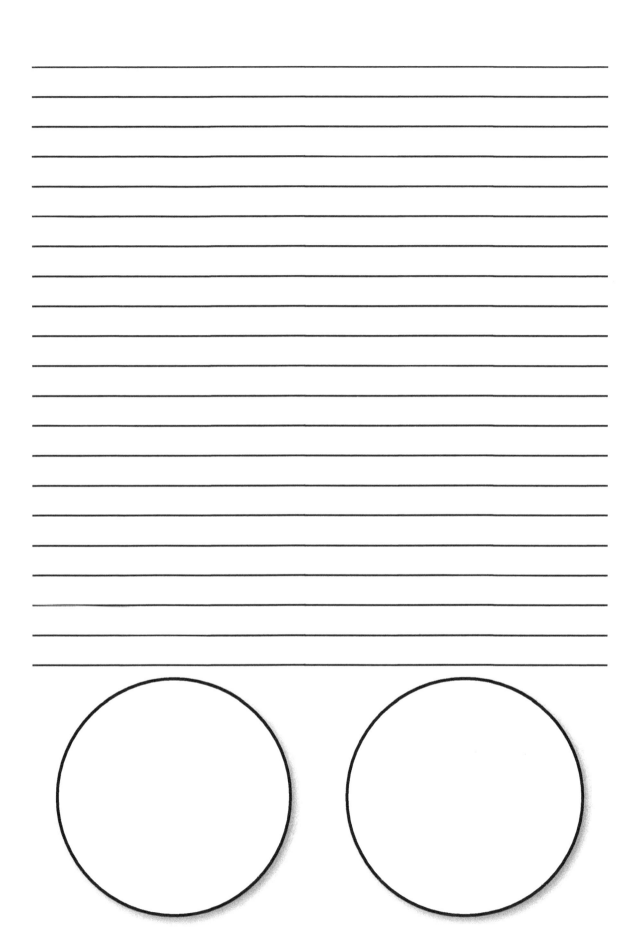

and settled at the bottom. Lalande A (8 mi. in diameter), located about 40 miles southwest of the crater Lalande, is a good example of a simple crater. With patience, good lighting, and decent optics you should be able to tell if Lalande A has a flat or rounded floor by looking at the shadow of the rim as it crosses the center of the floor. The rim shadow on a bowl-shaped floor will appear as a smooth arc. If the floor has partially filled, the shadow will be truncated (i.e., the apex will be squared off).

The neighborhood around Lalande and Mösting offers up many simple craters for your examination. Spend some time searching for evidence that they are either flat-floored or rounded. (Check out nearby Mösting A, for example, on the west rim of the flooded crater Flammarion, and sweep the area all around Lalande.) For the next step, a crater in transition between simple and complex, pay a visit to Hell (Really!) on Day 8 [SW/N9].

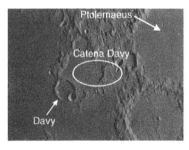

Catena Davy: [SW/L9] This fascinating crater chain was made when a comet or asteroid was torn into pieces by the gravitational pull of the Earth or the Moon. The alignment of smaller pieces flying through space then slammed into the Moon in machine-gun fashion, leaving a trail of small craters in a straight line. The largest of these craterlets is only a few miles wide and requires high magnification and good seeing.

This explanation of the origin of catenas was once a controversial idea, but in 1994 Comet Shoemaker-Levy silenced the critics when it slammed into Jupiter leaving the very same type of markings. When the comet hit Jupiter it released a mind-boggling 20 million megatons of energy. This would equal more than 30 billion Hiroshima bombs going off at the same time!

Straight Wall (Rupes Recta): [SW/M9] Two of the best-known faults on the Moon are *Rupes Recta* and *Rupes Cauchy* [Day 4]. They are fascinating to explore and they share remarkably similar neighborhoods: Both features are paralleled by a nearby rille (although

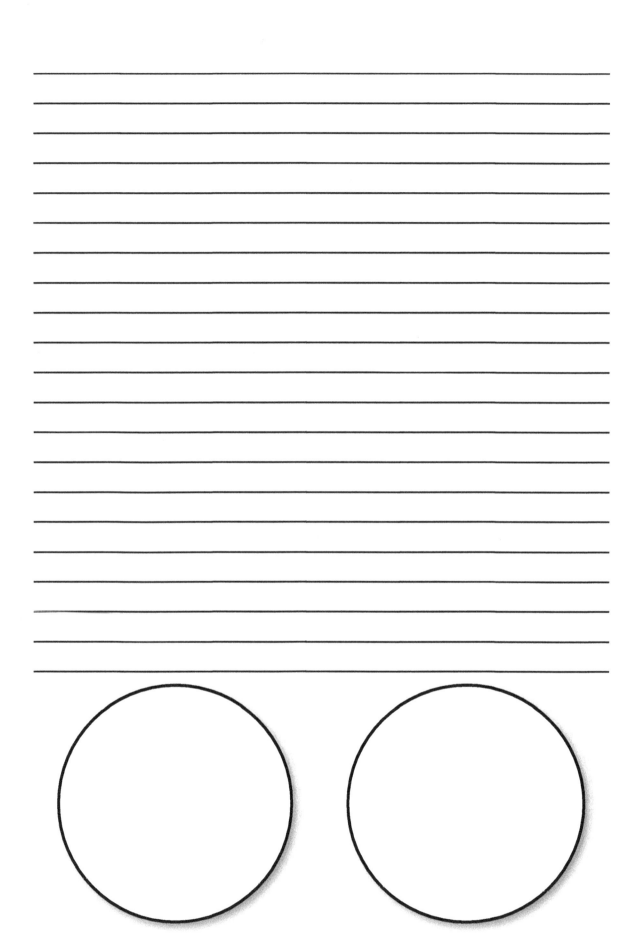

Rima Birt, the rille to the southwest of Straight Wall, needs a large telescope), and in each case, an intervening small crater separates the rille and the fault.

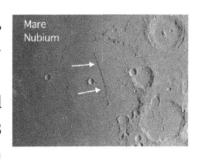

Straight Wall is the showpiece lunar fault line and can be seen clearly in the smallest telescopes. It is 68 miles long and between 800 and 1,000 feet high. If you view it either in the early morning on Day 8, or at lunar sunset around Day 22, you will see clear evidence that Straight Wall is an enormous fault line where the terrain to its west has fallen away. In the morning, the rising sun casts a thick black shadow over the lava plain to the west. At sunset two weeks later, the exposed slope of the fault is brightly illuminated.

At its south end, the Straight Wall terminates in what looks like a small arc of mountains. The effect of the ensemble makes Straight Wall look remarkably like a sword with handle and hilt. This arc of mountains is actually the remains of an ancient unnamed crater whose western side, like the Straight Wall itself, dropped as a result of faulting. When lava flows later flooded Mare Nubium they also covered the slumped western portion of this crater.

Birt: [SW/M9] Just to the west of Straight Wall is the small 10-mile crater Birt. Like Aristarchus (Day 11), Birt has interior bands running up its wall, although they are not as prominent. At 10 miles in diameter, Birt is on the small side, so it may not be immediately obvious.

Rima Birt: [SW/M9] If you are successful at locating the crater Birt, see if you can detect Rima Birt, a thin rille starting just to the west of the crater and continuing north. This will be a challenge. If you're not successful at first, keep coming back.

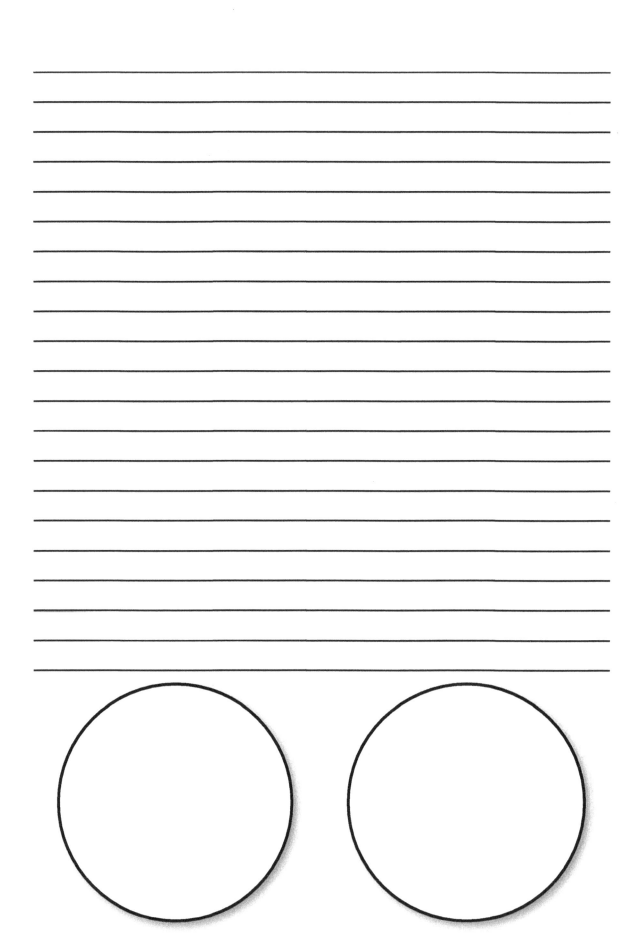

Lippershey:† [SW/M8] While you're in the neighborhood of Straight Wall, drop by and pay your respects to the simple crater **Lippershey**. As astronomers, we owe a lot to this crater's namesake. Without him there would be no telescopes!

Pitatus: [SW/M8] For several reasons, Pitatus is one of my favorite craters. For one thing, it is one of the best examples of a floor-fractured crater (FFC) on the Moon. Notice how shallow the crater is—an indication that the entire floor had been lifted up by the pressure of underlying magma. Look for the telltale arcuate

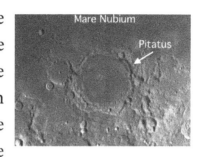

rilles around the inside perimeter—both are dependable signs that we have an FFC in our sights. Additionally, Pitatus has some very delicate features on its floor that will require a large aperture and steady seeing to resolve them.

If you can see some of the craterlets on the floor of Pitatus, keep observing them over the next several nights. They are secondary craters resulting from the formation of Tycho [Day 8; SW/P8] and their aspects will change with different lighting. The Tycho impact produced the most remarkable set of splash rays to be found on the Moon. Many of these rays are the result of lighter highland material being kicked up by secondary impacts from Tycho, not by Tycho itself. Such is the case here on the floor of Pitatus. Although rays become brighter (and craters tend to disappear) as the Sun rises, try to find a night when you can observe both craterlets *and* rays. With luck you will be able to see three lighter streaks pointing back to Tycho. Each streak begins at a cluster of small craters in the southern portion of Pitatus, the points of impact of debris that was blown in when Tycho was created.

I once made a cherry pie to celebrate my mom's 94th birthday (she was born on Feb. 22, George Washington's birthday). When I took the pie out of the oven,

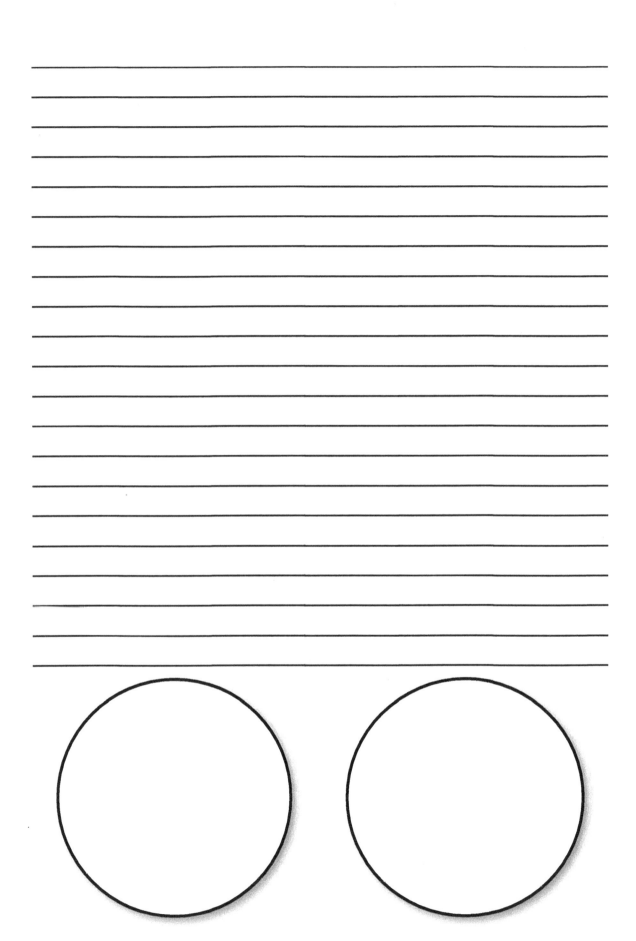

I noticed something oddly familiar about it. There was a striking resemblance to the crater Pitatus. As a result of similar processes that had been at work in their formation, both crater and pie were, essentially, "floor-fractured craters." After the

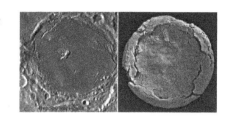

D A Y 8

"lava" had cooled in both objects (in the case of the pie, it was hot butter and flour), the level of their floors had dramatically shifted and arcuate cracks opened up as a result.[31] There was even a group of slightly off-center hills in the pie. I combined the images of both crater and pie and sent it to Charles Wood of *Sky and Telescope* for possible publication on his LPOD website (Lunar Photo of the Day). My mom's cherry pie actually made the big time and was published on LPOD for March 10, 2006. (Isn't it remarkable the things you can learn about astronomy in the kitchen?)

Hesiodus A: [SW/M8] Located just west of Pitatus is Hesiodus A, the Moon's best example of a ***concentric crater***, a type of crater that has a precisely cut out inner ring which makes the entire feature look a bit like a donut. In 1978, Charles Wood catalogued 51 such

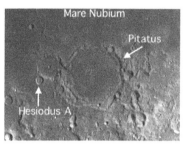

craters. He found that many of them are located near domes and rilles, and 70% are close to the edges of lunar seas, but so far scientists have not come to an agreement on their origins. Some say they are the results of simultaneous impacts, one on top of the other (but 51 such coincidences seems unlikely!). Others suggest volcanic activity. Nobody seems very sure, so enjoy the mystery!

Rima Hesiodus: [SW/N7-M8] The linear rille Rima Hesiodus is a graben (a special type of sunken parallel fault line) which connects with its namesake crater on

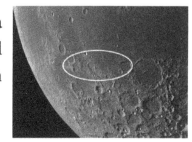

---

[31] To be precise, the rilles that opened up in the crater were the result of uplift, those in the pie were caused by subsidence—both important lunar processes.

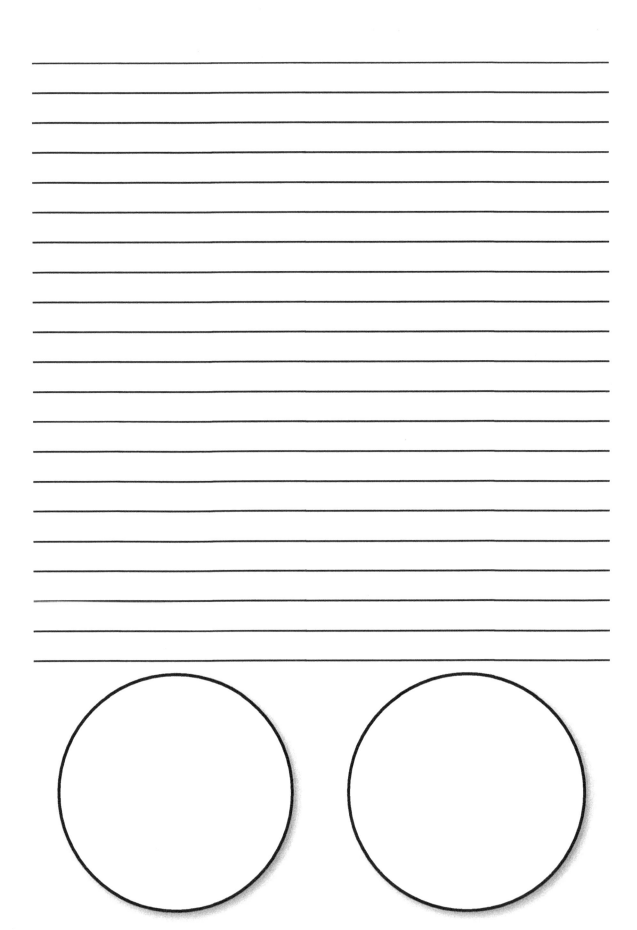

its eastern end and extends in a straight line for nearly 200 miles to the southwest across the charmingly named Palus Epidemiarum (the "Marsh of Epidemics"). The eastern part of this rille is revealed tonight.

Hell: [SW/N9] This crater (named after a Hungarian astronomer with an unfortunate last name) is an example of a transition crater. As the energy of an impact increases, craters go from smooth simple bowls to magnificent complex affairs with central mountain peaks, terraces, and ejecta blankets. Extensive slumping of the walls of Hell has left an untidy floor.

Tycho: [SW/P8] Tycho is one of the Moon's showpieces, both on Day 8 and around Full Moon when its system of rays becomes the dominant feature on the Moon. Tonight we get to see Tycho strutting about as the prototype of **complex craters** (which have terraced walls, central mountain peaks, flat floors, and ejecta blankets). The mountains around Tycho's rim, at their greatest height, soar almost 3 miles above its floor! Tycho is at the northern tip of a diamond formation of large and significant craters that include Maginus, Longomontanus, and Clavius. At a mere 109 million years, Tycho is also the youngest major crater on the Moon.

The explosion that blew out the Tycho crater has been estimated to be the equivalent of 30 trillion tons of TNT! To put this into perspective, imagine the energy that was released by the Hiroshima bomb. Now try to picture two million of those bombs going off at the same time! (The energy from the meteor impact that destroyed the dinosaurs equaled an incredible 100 trillion tons of TNT!)

When the asteroid that created Tycho hit, it would have been a spectacular sight. The dinosaurs had a front row seat to the event and would have been pelted for weeks with debris that had been blasted out of the site and made it all the way to Earth!

Much of the material that was blown out of the crater was instantly liquefied. It then rained back down

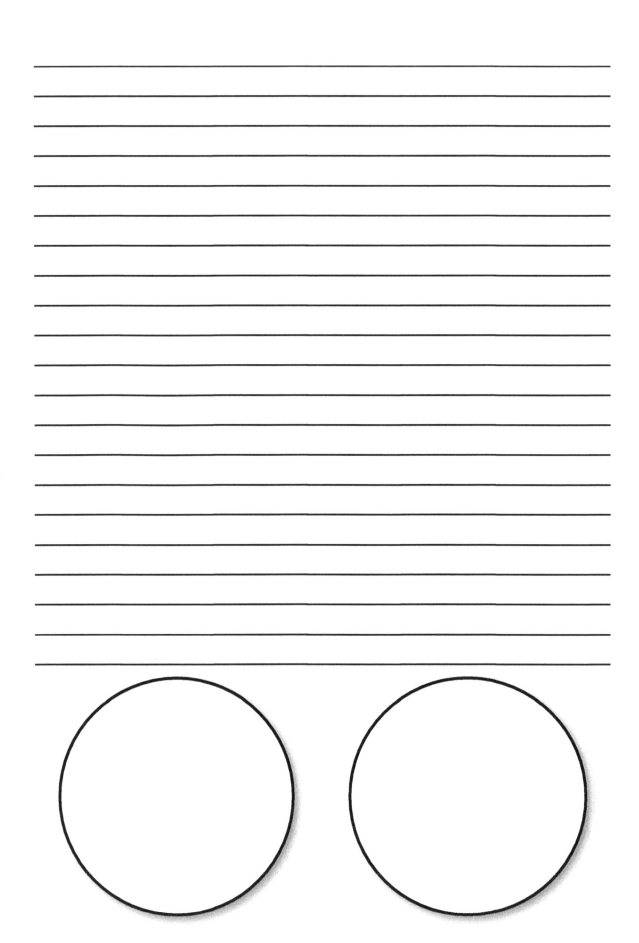

on the site and produced a veneer of **impact melt** that pooled smoothly on the
eastern portion of the floor.

Keep the image of Tycho in mind and compare it tomorrow night to Bullialdus
[M7]. This crater, with its terraced walls, central peaks, and flat floor mimics the
Tycho morphology more closely than any other crater in the southwest quadrant
of the Moon.

Maginus: [SW/Q9] Located at the eastern tip of the
diamond formation that includes Tycho, Longomontanus, and Clavius. Maginus has sometimes been
referred to as a "little Clavius" (the large crater just to
the SE of Maginus). Can you see the similarities?
There is a wealth of smaller detail within Maginus that is revealed by larger
telescopes. How much are you able to see?

Clavius: [Repeated from Day 7—SW/Q8] If you catch
the Moon at the end of Day 7 or early in Day 8 when
the terminator is around 15° (i.e., it cuts right through
Clavius), and if you have determined that you can see
objects that are as small as 2 arc-minutes with the naked
eye,[34] look at the Moon without benefit of telescope or binoculars and you might
be able to see a small notch that has been chiseled out of the terminator in the
southern portion of the Moon. This notch is the crater Clavius. If you need to,

> Clavius has been an object of special interest for astronomers ever since it was featured in
> the movie *2001*, which came out in the late 60s. It was in Clavius that aliens had buried
> the mysterious black monolith for a distantly anticipated race of intelligent hominids to
> discover. As a result of this discovery, the mind-expanding voyage to Jupiter was launched
> (*2001* was, after all, in the distant future at that time).

---

[34] See **resolution** in the *Glossary* for a method to determine how small an object you can see with your naked eyes.
This will probably vary between two and four arc-minutes.

doublecheck with binoculars then go back and see if you can detect it with your naked eyes.

Sunrise over Clavius is something that you don't want to miss! The crater is so large (140 miles) that the curvature of the Moon pushes the floor's central regions into the sunlight first. If you were an astronaut standing on this point, the Sun would be rising over a flat horizon—the rim mountains (some of them three miles high) would be below your line of sight!

As the day progresses the shadows will retreat to reveal a floor that is strewn with craterlets. There is a delightful arc of small craters, artistically and sequentially arranged in order of size, which begins at Rutherfurd, the larger crater just inside the southeast rim, arcs northward and then diminishes toward the west. These craterlets provide an excellent tool for amateur astronomers to test the resolution of their telescopes. In order of diminishing size they are Rutherfurd (34 miles), Clavius D (16 miles), C (12 miles), N (8 miles), J (7 miles), and JA (5 miles). In addition, there are upwards of 30 even smaller craterlets contained within this arc. If you can see several of these, then you have excellent optics indeed!

While the Sun angle is low over Clavius, look for several ridges that extend like fingers northward from Rutherfurd. The origin of these ridges remains a mystery. Revisit Clavius often. You will always see something that you missed previously.

Longomontanus: [SW/P7] Take a look at Longomon- 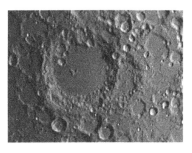 tanus and before reading further, decide if something seems slightly "wrong" about the crater. Longomontanus is an exception to the rule that crater age can be deter- mined by their relative sizes. Larger craters are almost always older, and when there's an overlap, smaller craters will intrude upon the rims and floors of their larger and older cousins. The east rim of Longo has superimposed itself on top of what is obviously an older but smaller crater.

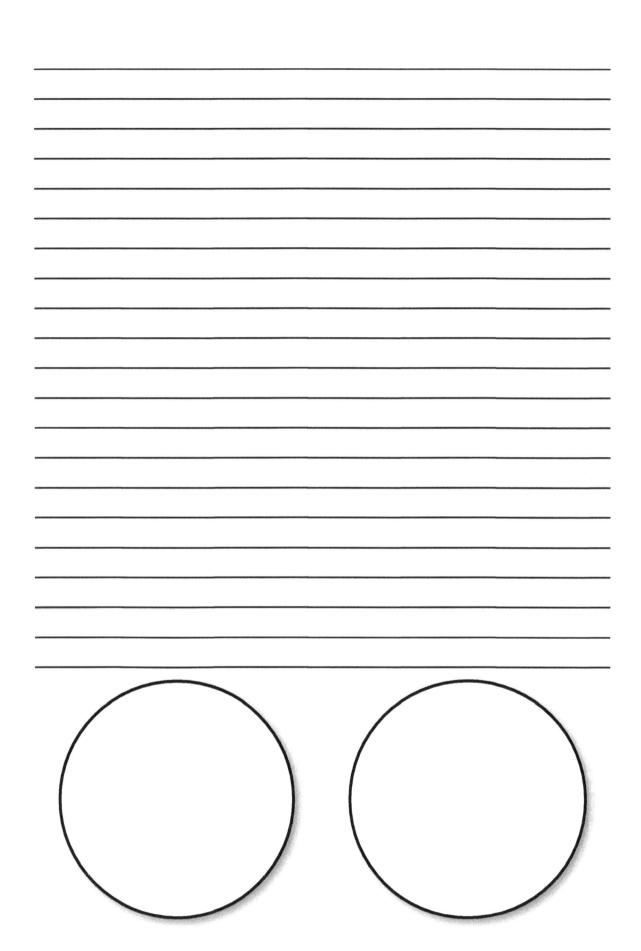

Day 9 (T=21° W)

Mare Frigoris: [NW-NE/D6-13] This is the only mare patch that isn't even roughly circular, although its northern boundary has an intriguing curve to it which may support the "Gargantuan hypothesis" (below). As the lunation progresses, you will notice how Mare Frigoris appears to connect Oceanus Procellarum to the eastern maria. It has been suggested that Frigoris is the northern rim of an enormous pre-nectarian feature called *Gargantuan Basin*, which spanned 1,500 miles from the western shores of Procellarum to the

middle of Mare Serenitatis. This is nearly 70% of the Moon's diameter and would have been an impressive wallop! As we get deeper into the lunar month, notice how Mare Frigoris extends itself to connect with Oceanus Procellarum, lending credence to the *Gargantuan* proposal.

Linné: [Repeated from Day 6—NE/G11] Linné is a simple, relatively young crater with an interesting history. It is 1.5 miles in diameter (only about 1.3 arc-seconds at the average distance of the Moon), which makes it about twice the size of **Meteor Crater** in Arizona. Linné is surrounded by very light-colored material, and because its appearance changes so much with different angles of illumination this was once taken as evidence that the Moon was not a totally dead place. Observe it over several days throughout the lunation and see if you would have come to the same conclusion.

Mare Imbrium: [Repeated from Day 8—±NW/F8] The Imbrium basin was created 3.9 billion years ago when an asteroid 60 miles in diameter slammed into the Moon at 10 miles per second and blasted out a 720-mile-wide crater!

Mare Imbrium, whose eastern portion is visible tonight, was at one time a spectacular **multi-ring basin** like Mare Orientale (see Day 13). Fortunately, segments of the original multi-ring features remain in the form of four stunning mountain ranges: the Alps, the Caucasus, the Apennines, and the Carpathians [±F10]. Unlike mountain ranges on the Earth, these ranges did not form by tectonic uplift; they were blasted into place by the impact that excavated Mare Imbrium (much like a billiard ball dropped into a tub of thick, viscous mud will leave a conspicuous circle of ridges around the point of impact). The Imbrium basin later filled up with lava that had the viscosity of hot maple syrup and therefore flowed very quickly, turning the mare basins into what were truly, for a time, liquid seas. (Early observers of the Moon weren't so far off base after all when they called these features "seas.")

Notice that the Alps have a smaller radius than the other three ranges. That's because they are part of the original *middle* ring. The Caucasus, Apennines, and Carpathians form the outer ring. The highest mountains in this outer ring rise to more than 18,000 feet (nearly 3½ miles—providing the best skiing in the solar system!). Remarkably, we are even able to catch glimpses of the inner ring (which has been almost entirely submerged beneath the lava flows). These are features in the form of isolated peaks and mountain ranges that poke up through the Imbrium plains and more or less form a circle around the center of Imbrium. The parts of the inner ring that you can see tonight are Montes Teneriffe [E8], Spitzbergen [F9], and Mons Pico [E9].

Charles Wood has made an intriguing suggestion that the Caucasus Mountain Range has actually rotated from its original alignment with the Alps. Examine the placement of the Caucasus carefully and see if you can agree with his proposition.

But there is an extra treat this evening. If the terminator is around 10° west, you should be able to see a distinct arcuate wrinkle ridge that begins

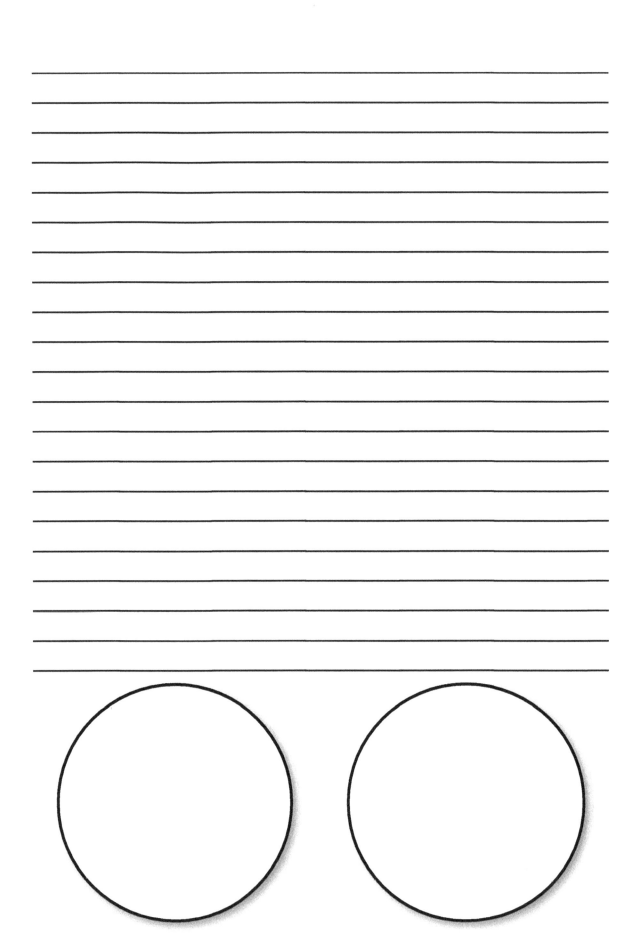

near Timocharis [G8], just touches the Spitzbergen Mountains, then curves to the north. Wrinkle ridges signal the presence of subsurface structures on the Moon—as breaking waves will sometimes indicate reefs lying just under the surface of the water. This long wrinkle ridge hovers immediately above the underlying mountain range that formed the inner ring of the Imbrium basin. The Spitzbergen Mountains are actually a part of this inner ring which has popped above the surface. Over the next few nights, see how far around the basin you can trace this ring.

Sinus Iridum: [NW/E6] (This feature may not be visible until tomorrow night.) Around the end of Day 9 and beginning of Day 10, when the terminator bisects Sinus Iridum, you will be able to catch the Jura Mountain Range when parts of it are in full sunlight. This produces an effect sometimes referred to as the "Golden Handle." (See *Day 10* for a full explanation of Sinus Iridum.)

Lambert-R: [NW/G7] Immediately south of the crater Lambert you will see what is called a "**ghost crater**"—a circular **wrinkle ridge** formation indicating an underlying crater that had been completely inundated by the Imbrium lava flows. As the lava cooled, it shrank and the outline of the original crater rim percolated to the top, leaving a ghostly imprint of the original crater.

Copernicus:† [NW/J7] Magnificent Copernicus has been justifiably dubbed "The Monarch of the Moon." The crater was blasted out 800 million years ago in an explosion that was so powerful that some of the ejected debris almost certainly rained down on the Earth. It is 58 miles in diameter and has walls that rise 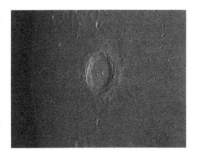 to an impressive 12,400 ft. above the floor. As a result, sunrise over Copernicus at the beginning of Day 9 is a thing of beauty! This single crater is large enough to enclose the entire state of Rhode Island. In the center there is a complex of

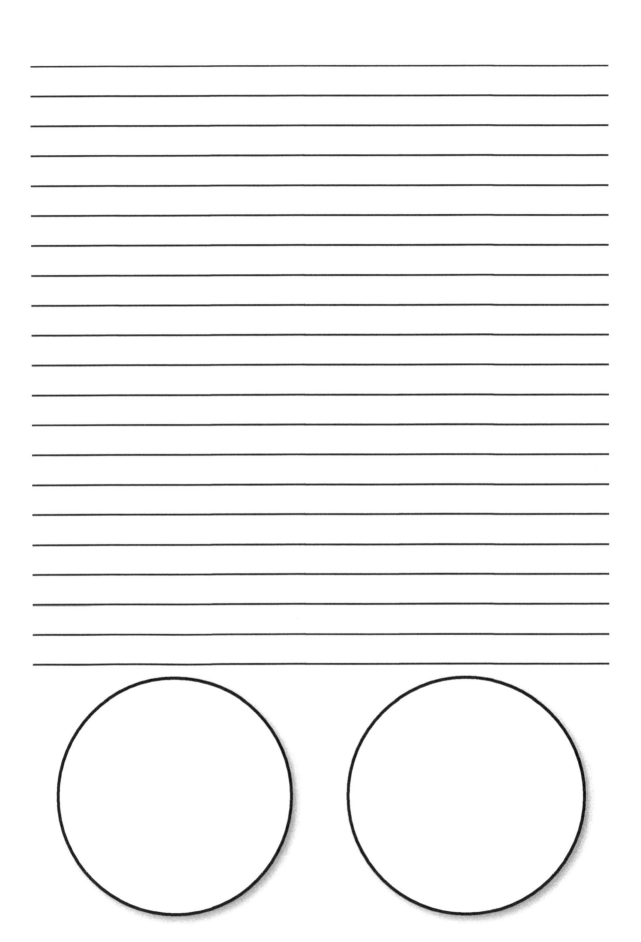

mountains that is worth studying. Some authorities say there are up to seven peaks. How many can you count?

See if you can spot the tiny crater Copernicus A (2.2 miles in diameter) on the east wall under the high rim peak. (It will be about 2 arc-seconds in diameter, so 100x or more should do the trick.)

There is a complex system of ridges radiating from Copernicus, and on the surrounding terrain between Copernicus and Eratosthenes you will find a host of **secondary craters** that resulted as huge boulders were blown out from the original impact and landed some distance away. These are some of the best secondaries on the Moon.

Immediately south of Copernicus is Fauth, a double crater that gives you the impression that you are peering at a keyhole.

Pytheas secondary craters: [NW/G7-8] The best place to see secondary craters that have landed within a **splash ray** is just 25 miles east of Pytheas. There is an alignment of seven or more secondary craters that are obviously confined within a long ray extending from Copernicus, 160 miles to the south. Tonight it is difficult to observe the connection with Copernicus because the craters are visible on Day 9, but the ray can be more clearly seen later at higher sun angles. So draw the alignment of craters tonight, then come back closer to Full Moon and fill in the splash ray.

Hortensius domes: [NW/J7] If you catch the terminator when it is about two-thirds of the way between Copernicus and Kepler (around Day 9 or the beginning of Day 10) you should be able to explore two fascinating dome fields around the craters Hortensius (J7) and Milichius (H6). **Domes**, by their very nature, are illusive objects and difficult to spot.

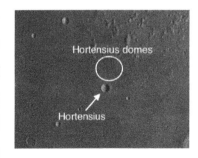

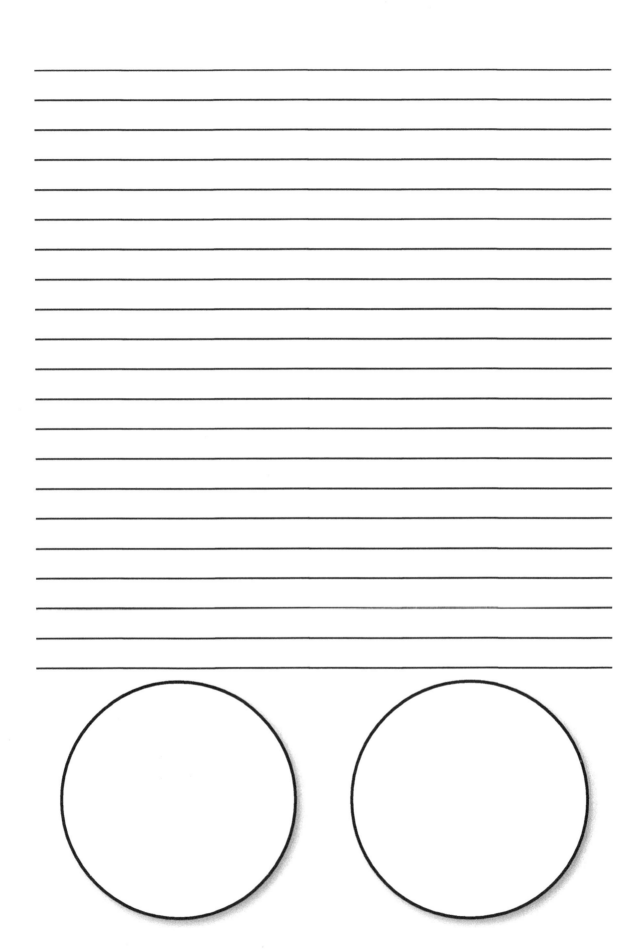

The easiest domes to find in this region are located two crater diameters WSW of Copernicus, just north of the 9-mile crater Hortensius. Here you will find a rich field of six domes, five of which have summit pits at the top. These pits are around 1 mile in diameter, which means they will subtend an angle of roughly one arc-second. If the atmosphere cooperates, seeing them will be an interesting and worthwhile challenge for both observer and telescope. If you can see the domes themselves, then wait patiently for the atmosphere to settle to spot the summit pits. Can you see them with less than a 10" instrument?

Milichius domes: [NW/J7] After visiting the Hortensius dome field, turn your telescope slightly northwest to the crater Milichius (about 7 miles in diameter).

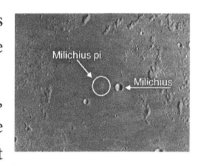

To its immediate west you will find a few domes, chief of which is Milichius π (pi), one of the more significant domes on the Moon. Milichius π is about 5 miles wide and has a summit crater a little over 1 mile in diameter. Because it is steeper than the average dome it is a little more prominent and will cast a longer shadow. (At the average distance of the Moon the summit pit would be about 0.9 arc-seconds in diameter, so it will be a challenge but keep trying.)

About 60 miles north of Milichius π you will run into another dome field just south of the 20-mile crater T. Mayer [H7]. This entire area, from Hortensius to T. Mayer, is chock-a-block full of domes and will reward close scrutiny.

Fra Mauro region: [SW/K8] Craters in the Fra Mauro region are critical to understanding an important process that shaped the Moon. For this reason, the *Apollo 14* astronauts, Alan Shepard and Ed Mitchell, landed just 20 miles north of Fra Mauro. Look closely at Fra Mauro and the three craters to its south—Parry,

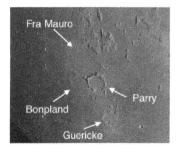

Guericke, and Bonpland. Look for the telltale gaps and gouges that cut through

their rims and point significantly back to Mare Imbrium, their place of origin. This is classic Imbrium sculpturing and is a textbook example of how you can "read" the lunar surface. Can you see the north-south linear features on Fra Mauro, Bonpland, and Parry? There is one long rille that breaches the walls of all three craters. What does this tell you about the age of these craters as they relate to Mare Imbrium? In many craters such as Alphonsus (Day 7; L9), Pitatus (Day 8; M8), and Posidonius (Day 5; F12), the rilles are clearly contained within the outer protective rims of the mountains, suggesting that they are related to the formation of the crater itself.

Bullialdus: [SW/M7] (Depending on libration, Bullialdus may not appear until tomorrow night.) If you recall what Tycho looked like last night (and there may be enough features left tonight to remind you), Bullialdus shares much of the same morphology in spite of being only half the size: a compound central mountain, eye-catching 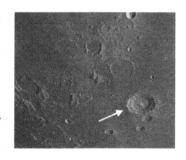 terraces, a flat floor, a thick ejecta blanket, and material in the immediate environs that rained back down after impact. There are so many interesting features that it is surprising that Bullialdus gets such short shrift. It is the most conspicuous crater on Mare Nubium, an area that offers several conversation pieces. Examine the inner terraces for tiny impact craters and evidence of landslides. Can you make out an intriguing raised ridge running from the central mountains southeast to the base of the terraces on the wall? Over the next few nights, observe how the appearance of the central mountains changes substantially.

The floor of Bullialdus creates a small illusion; as a result, there is some disagreement about its shape. Some observers think it is concave, others (most notably Patrick Moore, of Caldwell Object fame) think it is convex. How does it strike you?

Look carefully at the shared terrain between Bullialdus and Bullialdus A

immediately to its south. Other than the fact that Bullialdus A is smaller, can you see any evidence that tells you which crater is older?[35]

D A Y 9

Bullialdus Causeway:[36] [SW/M7] There is a wide, shallow valley that extends out from the west rim of Bullialdus and travels NW towards Lubiniezky. Toward the end of the valley (a little more than one crater diameter) you will run into two parallel lines, about 7 miles apart, running perpendicularly across the valley.

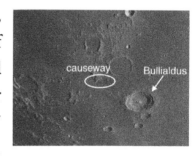

These parallel lines are clearly depicted on the *Field Map* as a short arc and give the illusion of a causeway or a bridge that cuts across the valley at right angles. (You'll need about 150x.) Whatever it is, it remains something of a mystery, and nobody has come up with an adequate explanation.

Moretus: [SW/R9] Although it lies very far south, Moretus is a beautiful complex crater that boasts one of the tallest central peaks (1.3 mi.) of any crater on the Moon. If it were more centrally located, it would be a major attraction!

Rima Hesiodus: [Repeated from Day 8—SW/N7-M8] The linear rille Rima Hesiodus is a graben (a special type of sunken parallel fault line) which connects with its namesake crater on its eastern end and extends in a straight line for nearly 200 miles to the southwest across the charmingly named *Palus Epidemiarum* (the

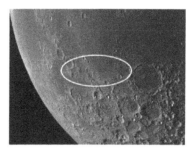

"Marsh of Epidemics"). The eastern part of this rille was revealed last night. Tonight you should be able to see its entire length. Notice how the rille slices straight through the mountains separating Nubium from Epidemiarum without so much as a hiccup. (Day 23 may give you a better view of the full length.)

---

[35] Bullialdus A has landed within the already formed ramparts of Bullialdus, making it younger. Also, the mere fact that it is smaller usually means it is also younger.

[36] This is a purely descriptive term as there is no official name for this feature.

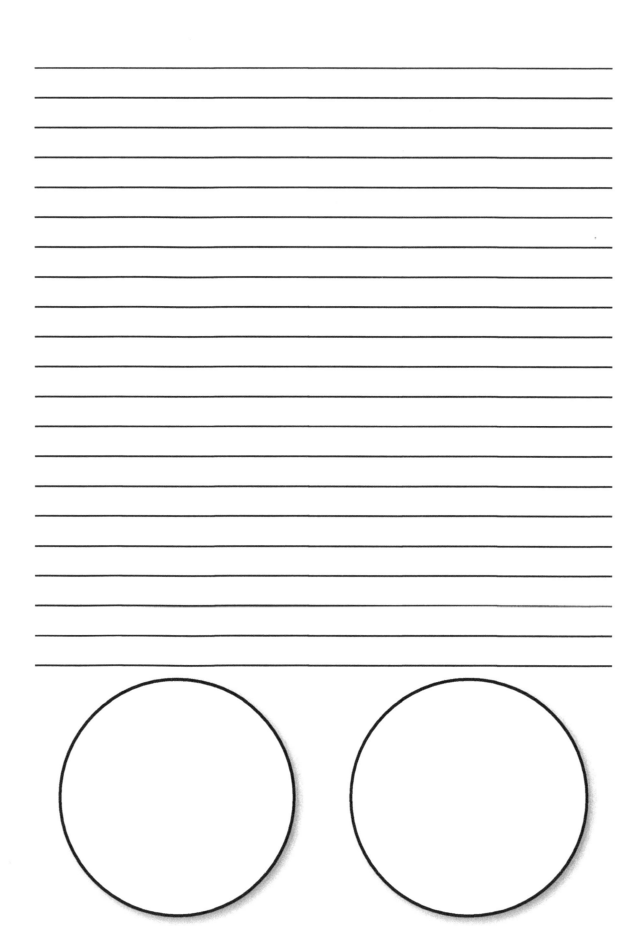

Marth: [SW/N7] Careful inspection of the unusual crater Marth (only 4.3 miles in diameter) reveals that it, like Hesiodus A [Day 8/M8] is a concentric crater. There are 51 such craters on the Moon. All of them are small and most of them lie near the edges of lunar seas. Marth's inner rim is taller than average (compare it to Hesiodus A which you saw last night). Scientists have yet to discover what causes these peculiar formations.

Rimae Ramsden: [SW/N6-7] If you continue following Rima Hesiodus to the southwest it will point to Rimae Ramsden, a network of rilles just east of the crater Ramsden. Like the Triesnecker rilles [Day 6/J10], scientists have no explanation of how they got there.

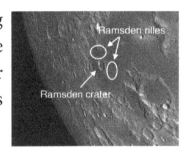

Kies π (pi): [SW/M7] Sandwiched in between Bullialdus and Rima Hesiodus you will find one of the Moon's best examples of a lunar **dome**, Kies π. Being located below the conspicuous crater Bullialdus and just west of the flooded crater Kies, it is one of the easiest domes to find. It is 7 miles in diameter, but because it is only 500

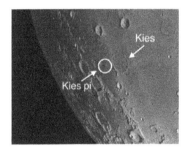

feet high you must catch it under a very low Sun. With luck, good optics, and a steady atmosphere you might be able to make out the 0.8 mile summit pit at the top. Most lunar domes occur in groups, so Kies π is something of an oddity.

Capuanus: [SW/N7] South of Kies π, just off the south shore of Palus Epidemiarum, is the lava-filled crater Capuanus that displays several low domes on its surface. You must observe these when the Sun is very low, but they should be easy objects for an eight-inch telescope. Domes are not usually found within craters, so this is a rarity.

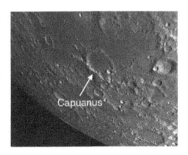

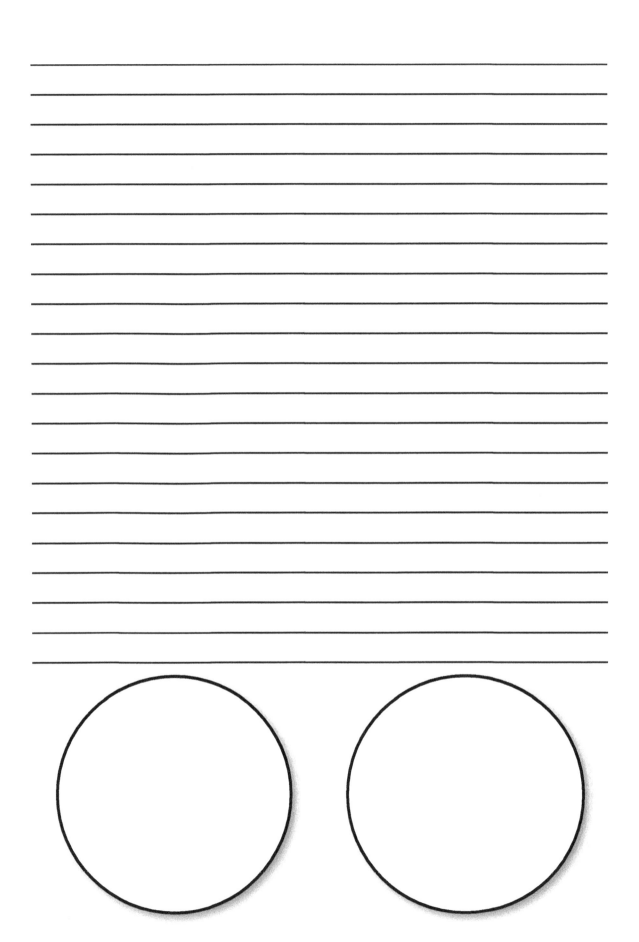

Rimae Hippalus: [SW/M6] On the east shore of Mare Humorum you will find the remnant of the crater Hippalus, whose southwest rim, because of **subsidence**, has disappeared into the mare. The area around Hippalus contains the finest examples of arcuate rilles to be found on the Moon. Each one is about 2

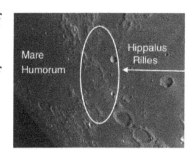

miles wide. (Catch these rilles when the terminator is around 32° west.) Notice how some of the rilles plough through mountain ridges and craters, and some are interrupted completely by small craters but continue on the other side. One prominent rille cuts straight through the middle of Hippalus. This gives you a clear indication of the sequence of activity. What features were in place before Humorum filled with lava and subsided? What features appeared after subsidence took place?

_____

_____

_____

_____

_____

_____

_____

_____

_____

_____

_____

_____

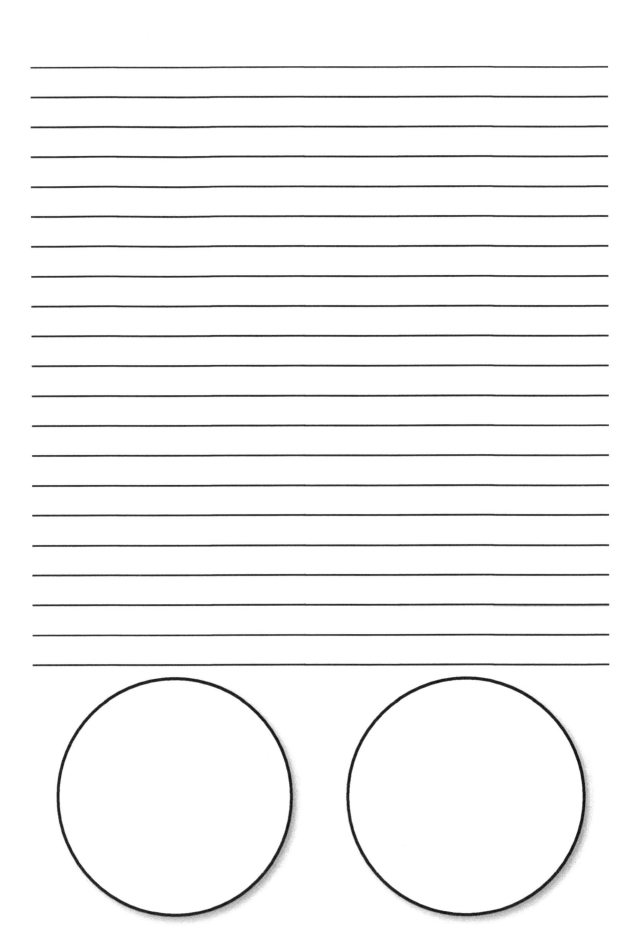

Day 10 (T= 28° W)

Mare Frigoris: [Repeated from Day 9—NW-NE/ D6-13] This is the only mare patch that isn't even roughly circular, although its northern boundary has an intriguing curve to it which may support the "Gargantuan hypothesis" (below). As the lunation progresses, you will notice how Mare Frigoris appears to connect Oceanus Procellarum to the eastern maria. It has been suggested that Frigoris is the northern rim of an enormous pre-nectarian feature called *Gargantuan Basin*, which spanned 1,500 miles from the western

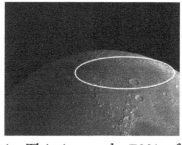

shores of Procellarum to the middle of Mare Serenitatis. This is nearly 70% of the Moon's diameter and would have been an impressive wallop! As we get deeper into the lunar month, notice how Mare Frigoris extends itself to connect with Oceanus Procellarum, lending credence to the *Gargantuan* proposal.

Mare Imbrium: [Repeated from Day 8—±NW/F8] The Imbrium basin (more than half of which you can see tonight) was created 3.9 billion years ago when an asteroid 60 miles in diameter slammed into the Moon at 10 miles per second and blasted out a 720-mile-wide crater!

Mare Imbrium was at one time a spectacular multi-ring basin like Mare Orientale (see Day 13). Fortunately, segments of the original multi-ring features remain in the form of four stunning mountain ranges: the Alps, the Caucasus, the Apennines, and the Carpathians [±F10]. Unlike mountain ranges on the Earth, these ranges did not form by tectonic uplift; they were blasted into place by the impact that excavated Mare Imbrium (much like a billiard ball dropped

into a tub of thick, viscous mud will leave a conspicuous circle of ridges around the point of impact). The
Imbrium basin later filled up with lava that had the viscosity of hot maple syrup and therefore flowed very
quickly, turning the mare basins into what were truly,
for a time, liquid seas. (Early observers of the Moon
were not so far off base after all when they called these
features "seas.")

> Charles Wood has made an intriguing suggestion that the Caucasus Mountain Range has actually rotated from its original alignment with the Alps. Examine the placement of the Caucasus carefully and see if you can agree with his proposition.

D A Y

10

Notice that the Alps have a smaller radius than the
other three ranges. That's because they are part of the original middle ring. The
Caucasus, Apennines, and Carpathians form the outer ring. The highest mountains in this outer ring rise to more than 18,000 feet (nearly 3½ miles—providing
the best skiing in the solar system!). Remarkably, we are even able to catch
glimpses of the inner ring. These are features in the form of isolated peaks and
mountain ranges that poke up through the Imbrium plains and more or less form
a circle around the center of Imbrium.

Sinus Iridum: [NW/E6] Sinus Iridum (the Bay of
Rainbows), located in the northwest sector of Mare
Imbrium, formed after the Imbrium impact but before
the lava flooding that filled the Imbrium basin. This
bay is itself an enormous 160-mile crater and is the
largest and most spectacular example of subsidence on
the Moon. If you have very sharp eyes, without optical
aid you might be able to see the "bite" that Iridum
takes out of Mare Imbrium. (You may have to wait
until tomorrow night.)

> As basins filled with heavy lava, many of them sank toward the center under the increased weight. As a result, shoreline craters would tilt inward and their seaward rims would often sink below "sea level," as happened here with Sinus Iridum.

When the Sun is at a low angle, you can see that Sinus Iridum is covered with
wrinkle ridges like so many waves lapping toward the shore.

The mountains on the rim of the bay have their own name, the Jura Mountains. They curve protectively around the bay and descend, because of the above-mentioned subsidence, to sea level where they terminate in capes at each end: Promontorium Laplace† on the northeast, and Promontorium Heraclides on the southwest.

Pay close attention to Promontorium Heraclides. Under the right lighting conditions around Day 10 you can see the profile of a woman's head with long flowing hair, as she gazes wistfully out into the bay. Those who have gotten to know her refer to her fondly as the *Moon Maiden*. **Cassini** himself was the first person to describe this feature. She reveals herself best when the seeing is a bit "soft" and the terminator has just cleared the western edge of the Jura Mountains. At this time you will see her gazing across the bay to Promontorium Laplace, her hair streaming out behind her. If the seeing is crisp, try defocusing a little.

Gruithuisen Gamma:[37] [NW/F5] There is a peninsula-like piece of highland terrain that extends southwest of Sinus Iridum. At the end of this peninsula you will find Mons Gruithuisen Gamma. Next to the so-called Valentine Dome, this is the Moon's second largest **dome**. If you can manage to spot the summit crater (3,000 feet

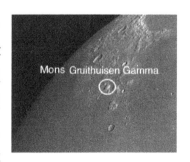

Mons Gruithuisen Gamma

in diameter, about one-half an arc-second at the Moon's mean distance), you will have accomplished a major feat! (This would require at least a 10" telescope and a night of exceptionally steady viewing.)

Mons Delisle: [NW/F-G6] The over-imaginative among us say that if you catch it in the right light this curved mountain range, located just southwest of Delisle crater, resembles a baby with an oversized head, two outstretched arms, and trailing legs. The baby is speedily crawling southward not far from a nearby unnamed

---

[37] Pronounced /GROOT.hoo.zen/. For Baron von Gruithuisen's interesting history see "Lunar City" on Day 7.

mountain group to its northwest which has informally been named "the Skull." Your creative challenge for the evening is to see if you can turn the above named features into a baby and a skull.

Kepler:† [NW/J6] Kepler is a substantial 20-mile crater with terraced walls and some disappointingly feeble hills in place of a central mountain peak. There is a peculiar straight gash just in from the east rim which forms a long straight valley. Revisit Kepler at Full Moon to appreciate how its rays intertwine with those of Copernicus and Aristarchus.

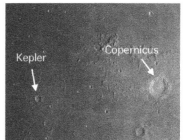

Bullialdus: [Repeated from Day 9—SW/M7] If you recall what Tycho looked like last night (and there may be enough features left tonight to remind you), Bullialdus shares much of the same morphology in spite of being only half the size: a compound central mountain, eye-catching terraces, a flat floor, a thick

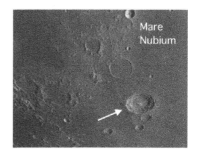

ejecta blanket, and material in the immediate environs that rained back down after impact. There are so many interesting features that it is surprising that Bullialdus gets such short shrift. It is the most conspicuous crater on Mare Nubium, an area that offers several conversation pieces. Examine the inner terraces for tiny impact craters and evidence of landslides. Can you make out an intriguing raised ridge running from the central mountains southeast to the base of the terraces on the wall? Over the next few nights, observe how the appearance of the central mountains changes substantially.

The floor of Bullialdus creates a small illusion; as a result, there is some disagreement about its shape. Some observers think it is concave, others (most notably Patrick Moore, of Caldwell Object fame) think it is convex. How does it strike you?

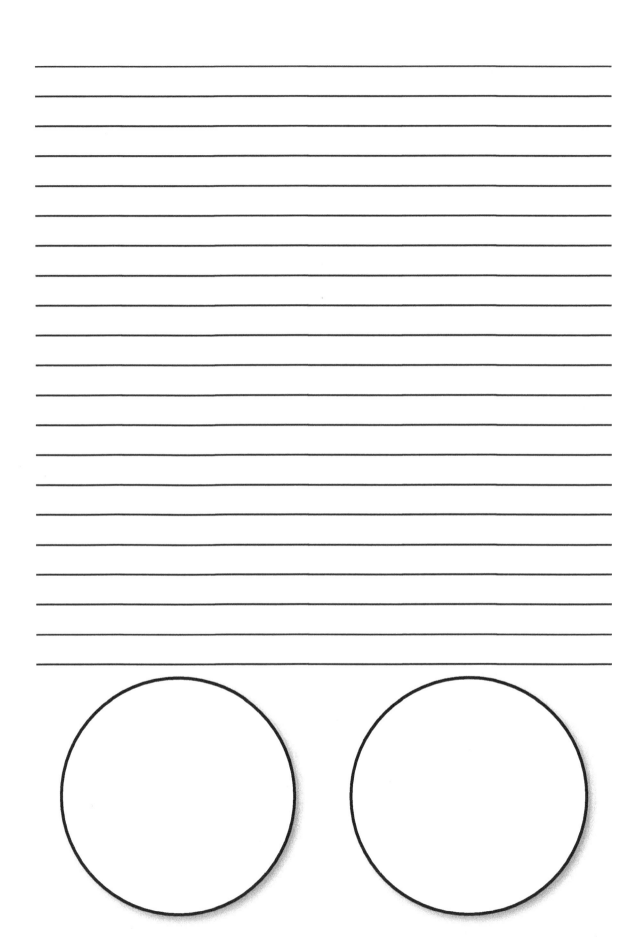

Look carefully at the shared terrain between Bullialdus and Bullialdus A immediately to its south. Other than the fact that Bullialdus A is smaller, can you see any evidence that tells you which crater is older? [38]

Bullialdus Causeway:[39] [Repeated from Day 9—SW/M7] There is a wide, shallow valley that extends out from the west rim of Bullialdus and travels NW towards Lubiniezky. Toward the end of the valley (a little more than one crater diameter) you will run into two parallel lines, about 7 miles apart, running

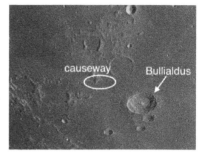

perpendicularly across the valley. These parallel lines are clearly depicted on the *Field Map* as a short arc and give the illusion of a causeway or a bridge that cuts across the valley at right angles. (You'll need about 150x.) Whatever it is, it remains something of a mystery, and nobody has come up with an adequate explanation.

Rimae Ramsden: [Repeated from Day 9—SW/N6-7] If you continue following Rima Hesiodus to the southwest it will point to Rimae Ramsden, a network of rilles just east of the crater Ramsden. Like the Triesnecker rilles [Day 6/J10], scientists have no explanation of how they got there.

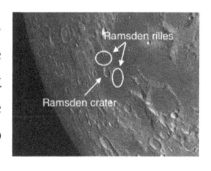

Mare Humorum: [SW/M6] The Humorum basin is one of the best examples of *subsidence* that you can see on the Moon. As the basin sank under the weight of its lavas, arcuate cracks, which can be easily observed in small telescopes, opened up on the east

---

[38] Bullialdus A has landed within the already formed ramparts of Bullialdus, indicating that it's younger. Also, the mere fact that it is smaller usually means it is younger.

[39] A purely descriptive term as there is no official name for this feature.

side around Hippalus and on the west side. The craters Doppelmayer, Lee, Hippalus, and Loewy tilted inward and their seaward rims sank beneath the lava flows which covered Mare Humorum.

Gassendi: [SW/L5] Three generations of crater age can be easily observed on Mare Humorum. In descending order of age we have Mare Humorum itself,[40] which is overlapped by the younger crater Gassendi on the north rim, which in turn is overlapped on its north rim by Gassendi A. (Both

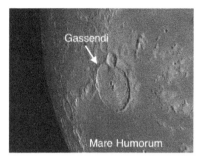

Gassendis taken together are sometimes referred to as the diamond ring.) The usually dependable rule in play here is that smaller craters are younger (there are some exceptions). The invariably dependable rule is that the topmost overlapping crater is *always* younger.

Gassendi is a double prize in that it is a **floor-fractured crater** with a nice set of central mountain peaks, the highest of which rises to 4,000 feet. It is also a textbook example of **subsidence**.[41] Notice how there is a small amount of smooth mare inundation near the SE portion of the rim.

Gassendi is considered to be one of the Moon's most beautiful and interesting objects. To add to the interest, its floor is crisscrossed by a plethora of rilles (some authorities say there are at least 30). Several rilles in the southeast section can be easily seen with a 4-inch scope. The ones on the eastern half require larger apertures. Draw a map of what you can see,

The feature at the top of Gassendi is not the only diamond ring in the heavens. Take your binoculars (you'll need a 2° field) and focus on the North Star. You will notice a circlet of 7th and 8th magnitude stars which forms what is called "the Engagement Ring" with Polaris as the centerpiece.

---

[40] A mare (sea) is nothing more than a large crater that has been filled in with lava.

[41] Due to dramatic subsidence, the walls of Gassendi slope down from a height of 6,100 ft. to a mere 200 ft. There seems to be one small breach where it looks like the wall has fallen almost to sea level.

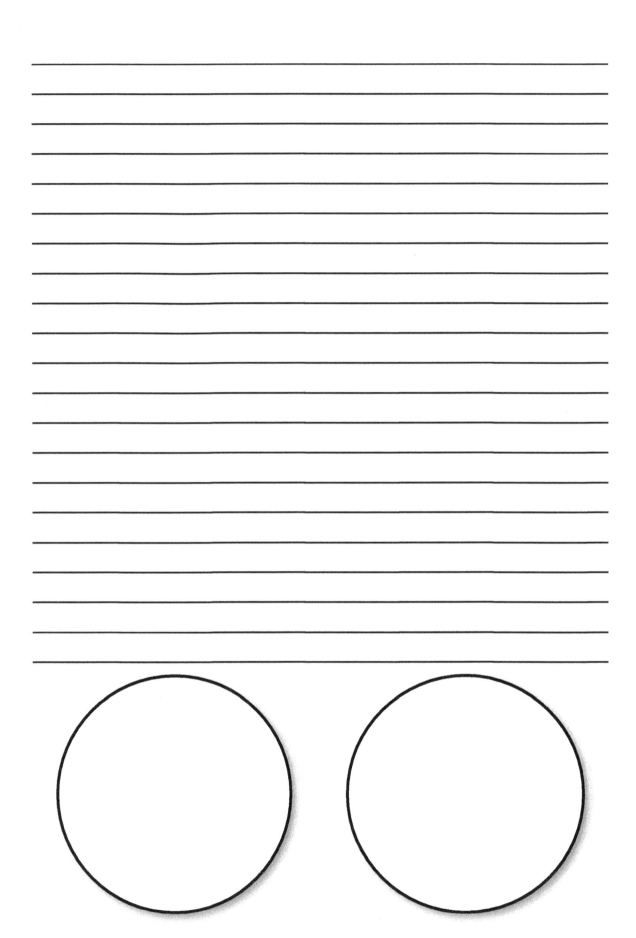

then come back later and try to improve on the count. (See how close you can get to 30.) Because its interior features change noticeably as the Sun rises higher, it is a rare event that any two observers will agree on the number and placement of the rilles. (You will probably discover that you will not agree even with *yourself* after visiting a few times.)

**D
A
Y

10**

While you're in the area of Gassendi, be on the lookout for LTP's. Several have been reported here.

Gassendi A: [SW/L6] This is the gemstone in the "diamond ring" mentioned above (the small unnamed crater at the top of Gassendi). Although Gassendi A is much smaller than Gassendi, its walls are one mile higher because it is not a **floor-fractured crater**, i.e., underlying pressure never caused its floor to rise abnormally, as is the case with Gassendi.

Schiller: [SW/Q6] Schiller is a curiosity. It has the appearance of an unusually elongated crater, but there is no process that could create one crater with such an extremely elongated axis; however, there is no indication on the floor of separate impacts. The current belief is that Schiller was created when a flight of three or

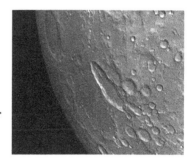

four projectiles landed at virtually the same moment. The liquefied target zones then blended together to leave no trace of separate impacts.

Just to the southwest of Schiller there is an unnamed basin which shows striations from lunar material that was blasted out of the Orientale basin [Day 13], located just around the southwest limb of the Moon in the L-M libration zone on your *Field Map*.

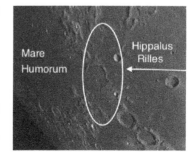

Mare Humorum

Hippalus Rilles

Rimae Hippalus: [Repeated from Day 9—SW/M6] On the east shore of Mare Humorum you will find the remnant of the crater Hippalus whose southwest rim,

because of **subsidence**, has disappeared into the mare. The area around Hippalus contains the finest examples of arcuate rilles to be found on the Moon. Each one is about 2 miles wide. (Catch these rilles when the terminator is around 32° west.) Notice how some of the rilles plough through mountain ridges and craters, and some are interrupted completely by small craters but continue on the other side. One prominent rille cuts straight through the middle of Hippalus. This gives you a clear indication of the sequence of activity. What features were in place before Humorum filled with lava and subsided? What features appeared after subsidence took place?

D A Y 10

Newton:† [SW/S8] Newton is the deepest crater on the Moon! Since its rim walls rise to 29,000 feet, they are as high as Mt. Everest! It's a pity that the crater named after the greatest scientist who ever lived is located so close to the lunar south pole. As a result, it's best to wait until there is a strong libration in latitude (around -5°).

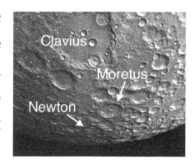

_____

_____

_____

_____

_____

_____

_____

_____

_____

_____

Day 11 (T=39° W)

D A Y 11

One of the more fascinating regions on the Moon is revealed tonight. It is the area around the Aristarchus Plateau [G4-5] that includes Aristarchus, Herodotus, and Schröter's Valley. Sunrise over this region is a particularly fetching sight.

Mare Frigoris: [Repeated from Day 9—NW-NE/ D6-13] This is the only mare patch that isn't even roughly circular, although its northern boundary has an intriguing curve to it which may support the "Gargantuan hypothesis" (below). As the lunation progresses, you will notice how Mare Frigoris appears

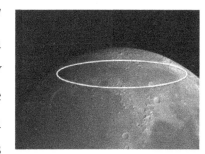

to connect Oceanus Procellarum to the eastern maria. It has been suggested that Frigoris is the northern rim of an enormous pre-nectarian feature called *Gargantuan Basin*, which spanned 1,500 miles from the western shores of Procellarum to the middle of Mare Serenitatis. This is nearly 70% of the Moon's diameter and would have been an impressive wallop! As we get deeper into the lunar month, notice how Mare Frigoris extends itself to connect with Oceanus Procellarum, lending credence to the *Gargantuan* proposal.

Mare Imbrium: [Repeated from Day 8—±NW/F8] The Imbrium basin is so large that it has now taken four days to completely reveal it. It was created 3.9 billion years ago when an asteroid 60 miles in diameter slammed into the Moon at 10 miles per second and blasted out a 720-mile-wide crater which is revealed in its entirety tonight.

Mare Imbrium was at one time a spectacular **multi-ring basin** like Mare Orientale (see Day 13). Fortunately, segments of the original multi-ring features remain in the form of four stunning mountain ranges: the Alps, the Caucasus, the Apennines, and the Carpathians [±F10—best seen around Days 7-8]. Unlike mountain ranges on the Earth, these ranges did not form by tectonic uplift; they were blasted into place by the impact that excavated Mare Imbrium (much like a billiard ball dropped into a tub of thick, viscous mud will leave a conspicuous circle of ridges around the point of impact).

The Imbrium basin later filled up with lava that had the viscosity of hot maple syrup and therefore flowed very quickly, turning the mare basins into what were truly, for a time, liquid seas. (Early observers of the Moon were not so far off base after all when they called these features "seas.")

**D
A
Y
11**

Sinus Iridum: [Repeated from Day 10—NW/E6] Sinus Iridum (the Bay of Rainbows), located in the northwest sector of Mare Imbrium, formed after the Imbrium impact but before the lava flooding that filled the Imbrium basin. This bay is itself an enormous 160-mile crater and is the largest and

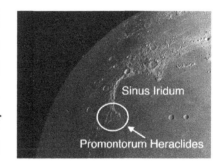

most spectacular example of subsidence on the Moon. If you have very sharp eyes, without optical aid you should be able to see the "bite" that Iridum takes out of Mare Imbrium.

When the Sun is at a low angle, you can see that Sinus Iridum is covered with **wrinkle ridges** like so many waves lapping toward the shore.

The mountains on the rim of the bay have their own name, the Jura Mountains. This wall of mountains curves protectively around the bay and descends, because of the above mentioned subsidence, to sea level

As basins filled with heavy lava, many of them sank toward the center under the increased weight. As a result, shoreline craters would tilt inward and their seaward rims would often sink below "sea level," as happened here with Sinus Iridum.

where they terminate in capes at each end: Promontorium Laplace† on the northeast and Promontorium Heraclides on the southwest.

Pay close attention to Promontorium Heraclides. Under the right lighting conditions around Day 10 you can see the profile of a woman's head with long flowing hair. Those who have gotten to know her refer to her fondly as the *Moon Maiden*. **Cassini** himself was the first person to describe this feature. She reveals herself best when the seeing is a bit "soft" and the terminator has just cleared the western edge of the Jura Mountains. At this time you will see her gazing across the bay to Promontorium Laplace, her hair streaming out behind her. If the seeing is crisp, try defocusing a little.

Aristarchus Plateau: [NW/G4-5] The plateau is a diamond shaped feature with straight sides measuring 100 x 125 miles and is over a mile higher than the surrounding mare areas. It is conjectured that the plateau was uplifted because of the pressures exerted by underground magma. It is an unusual

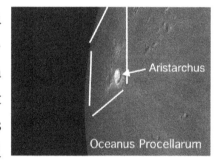

object not only because of its straight sides but because it is covered by a mantle of pink-colored pyroclastic ash 30 to 100 feet thick. The plateau has attracted the attention of NASA as an area for lunar colonization because hydrogen and oxygen can be extracted from the ash, providing fuel, water, and breathable air.

The ash on the Aristarchus Plateau is the very kind of stuff that NASA was concerned about for the Apollo program. Landing in 30 feet of lunar dust would not have gone well for the astronauts! Their solution was to use the 24" telescope on Mt. Wilson to determine safe landing sites by using infrared imaging (lunar dust reflects heat differently than solid terrain). This historic telescope is now in the possession of the Little Thompson Observatory in Berthoud, Colorado. The observatory is open to the public every night of the year and groups can reserve it, free of charge, for guided presentations by going to *www.starkids.org*.

The reddish color of the plateau is distinctive and sets it apart from the gray of the surrounding terrain. (Other observers see greenish or yellowish tones. What do you see?)

Aristarchus:† [NW/G5] Aristarchus is the brightest spot on the Moon, a phenomenon which you observed on Day 3 when you noticed that it even became visible on the dark portion of the Moon. It is so bright that Sir William Herschel[42] mistook it for an erupting volcano. Depending on libration, it will come into view around the end of Day 10.

Can you make out the dark radial bands which climb straight up the west wall? (They will become more prominent as the Sun rises.) Because the Aristarchus impact straddled the boundary between Imbrium and the Aristarchus Plateau, it excavated very different types of material and these multi-hued bands were the result. How many can you see? Two or three are easily visible in a 3" refractor, but some observers have reported seeing up to nine bands! Make a drawing of what you see, then come back later and try to add to the number. Do the bands become more or less prominent as the Sun rises over Aristarchus? As lighting conditions change, you might be able to see the bands creep up the wall and spill over onto the lunar terrain beyond.

During the *Apollo 11* flight, as they were observing the lunar surface through binoculars, Armstrong, Collins and Aldrin reported seeing a luminosity emanating from the northeast wall of Aristarchus. Observations made from Earth-based telescopes at the same time confirmed what seemed to be a genuine sighting of an LTP.

When observing Aristarchus keep your eyes peeled for LTP's—just don't hold your breath.

---

[42] 18th c. English astronomer who discovered Uranus.

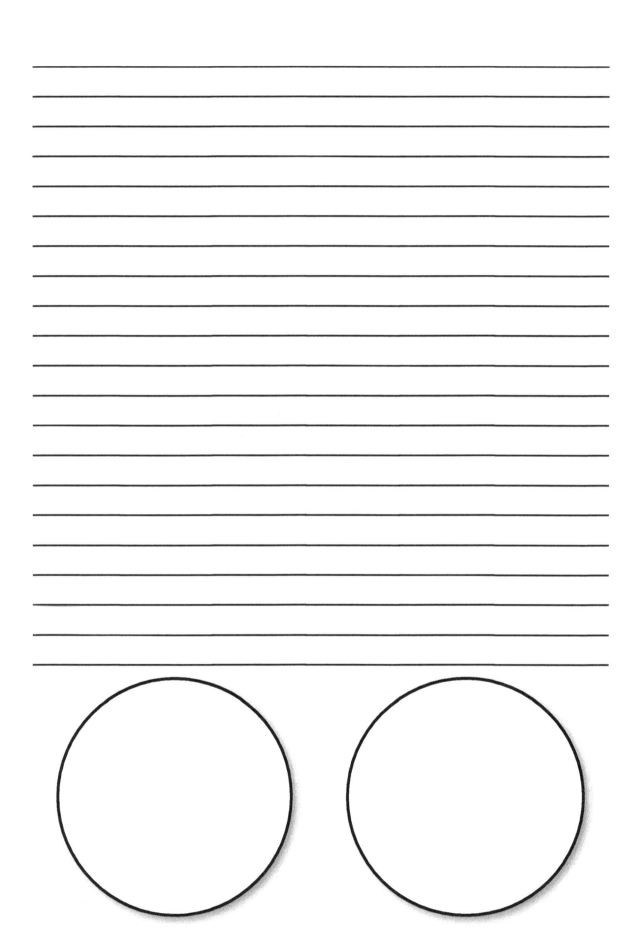

Schröter's Valley/Cobra Head: [NW/G5-4] Schröter's Valley is the Moon's most impressive sinuous rille and was created when a monstrous **lava tube** collapsed. It begins at a volcano that is popularly known as "the Cobra Head" and then meanders for 100 miles toward Oceanus Procellarum. For most of its length it varies between three and six miles wide and

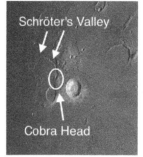

is up to 3,000 feet deep. It is estimated that at the peak of its activity an incredible 10 million tons of lava *per second* flowed through Schröter's Valley! At the end of its 100-mile journey the lava dramatically cascaded over a 3,000-foot-high cliff into Oceanus Procellarum, which it then filled to a depth of 600 feet!

Marius Hills: [NW/H4] Immediately north and west of the crater Marius is the largest dome field on the Moon, the Marius Hills. Because domes are such low features, you must observe them when the **terminator** is close. These hills are a combination of low domes, around 1,000 feet high, and steeper volcanoes with genuine

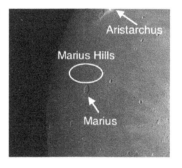

cones that go up to 3,000 feet. There are over 300 such formations in this area!

About one crater-diameter south of Marius, in the center of a circular depression, there is a single unnamed dome with a summit pit. Because it is 6 miles in diameter it is curious that it remains unnamed. See if you can make it out.

Rima Marius: [NW/H4-5] Just to the northwest of the crater Marius C is Rima Marius, a sinuous rille that extends for 150 miles. When the rille starts out it is about 1.2 miles wide (~1 arc-second), but it tapers down to only .3 miles. Because a line can be easily distinguished when a point of the same diameter is totally invisible, you should be able to see the rille when its width is well below the theoretical limits of your telescope. See how far you can extend Rima Marius across the lunar surface.

Mare Humorum: [Repeated from Day 10—SW/M6] The Humorum basin is one of the best examples of *subsidence* that you can see on the Moon. As the basin sank under the weight of its lavas, arcuate cracks, which can be easily observed in small telescopes, opened up on the east side around Hippalus and on the

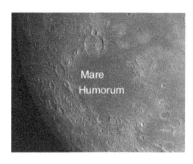

west side. The craters Doppelmayer, Lee, Hippalus, and Loewy tilted inward and their seaward rims sank beneath the lava flows which covered Mare Humorum.

Look closely at the Hippalus rilles just east of the mare. Notice how some of them plough through both mountain ridges and craters, and some are interrupted completely by small craters but continue on the other side. This gives you a clear indication of the sequence of activity. What features were in place before Humorum filled with lava and subsided? What features appeared after subsidence took place?

Letronne: [SW/L5] Notice the similarities between Gassendi (Day 10) and Letronne. They are both examples of subsidence, except that Latronne's seaward rim has been completely covered by lava—so much so that it looks like a small version of Sinus Iridum [NW/E6] which also came into view last night and is still promi-

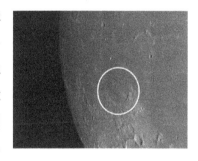

nent this evening. In the very middle of Letronne there is an example of a **wrinkle ridge** that outlines a ghost crater lying beneath the surface.

Doppelmayer: [SW/M5] Doppelmayer, on the southwest shore of Humorum, is a classic example of crater subsidence. The inundated top of the north rim of Doppelmayer is so close to the surface that, under low lighting, we can see its ghost image bleeding through to the surface as a **wrinkle ridge**.

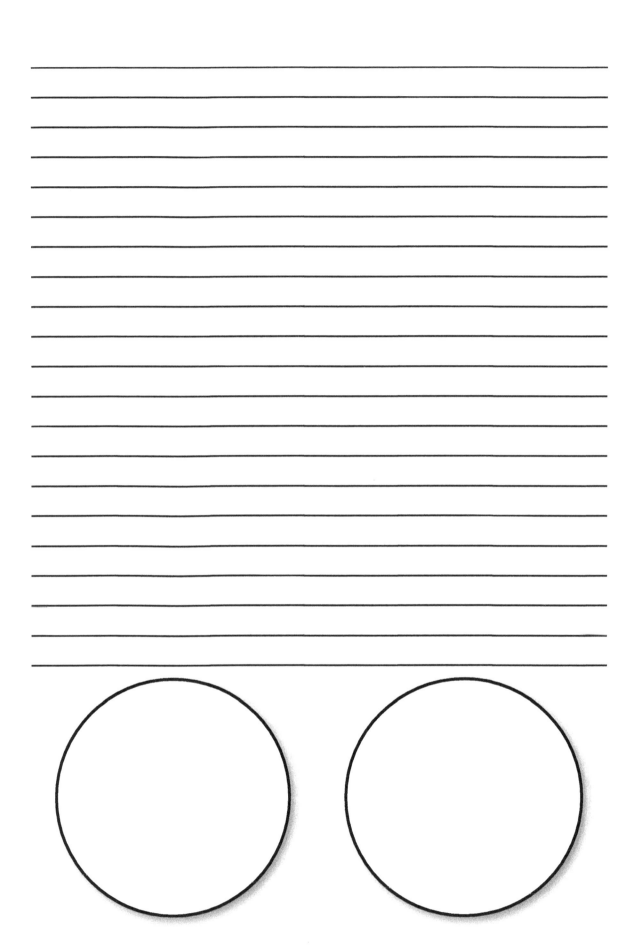

de Gasparis rilles: [SW/M4] The crater de Gasparis, just to the west of Humorum, is a hub of rille activity. With no fewer than nine rilles converging on or near it, de Gasparis, like Triesnecker [Day 6], looks like a railway switchyard. Add to this the Mersenius rilles just to the northeast and we have a very busy neighborhood indeed.

**D
A
Y
11**

_____

_____

_____

_____

_____

_____

_____

_____

_____

_____

_____

_____

_____

_____

_____

_____

Day 12 (T=54° W)

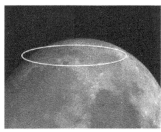

D A Y 12

Mare Frigoris: [Repeated from Day 9—NW-NE/D6-13] This is the only mare patch that isn't even roughly circular, although its northern boundary has an intriguing curve to it which may support the "Gargantuan hypothesis" (below). As the lunation progresses, you will notice how Mare Frigoris appears to connect Oceanus Procellarum to the eastern maria. It has been suggested that Frigoris is the northern rim of an enormous pre-nectarian feature called *Gargantuan Basin*, which spanned 1,500 miles from the western shores of Procellarum to the middle of Mare Serenitatis. This is nearly 70% of the Moon's diameter and would have been an impressive wallop! See if you can trace the entire outline of this putative basin tonight. Do you think the *Gargantuan* proposal has merit?

Mons Rümker: [NW/E4] Unfortunately this feature is too close to the Moon's limb to see it very clearly. In spite of its name, Mons Rümker is not really a mountain, it's an extensive complex of domes. The diameter of the formation is over 40 miles. Although there are about a dozen domes here, through a telescope it looks like a mound with a bumpy surface.

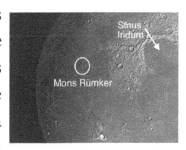

Hevelius: [NW/J3] Hevelius is a large 66-mile crater just north of Grimaldi on the western shore of Procellarum. It is a moderately complex object with terraced walls that rise to 6,000 feet, a central hill, at least seven internal craters (how many can you see?) and a system of crisscrossing rilles that require a very low

angle sun to become visible. Can you tell if the simple crater just in from the NW rim has a flat or rounded floor?

Reiner Gamma: [NW/J4] Lunar swirls are absolutely flat features that cast no shadows but leave enigmatic whorl-like markings on the lunar surface. No known geological process could have created them, and to heighten the mystery, instruments on Apollo spacecraft measured

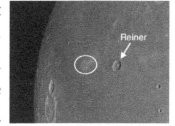

strong magnetic fields directly over the swirls. For the fanciful, they are eerily reminiscent of crop circles. Of the three swirls on the Moon, two have been found to be **antipodal** features of major impact zones and mascons. All three of the swirls on the Moon (there are two on the far side) are associated with strong magnetic anomalies.

Grimaldi: [SW/K3] In comparison to Aristarchus (Day 11), which is the brightest spot on the Moon, Grimaldi is the darkest. Sunrise over Grimaldi is quite a lovely sight. The rim around Grimaldi has been heavily eroded by subsequent impacts, but once the floor is illuminated

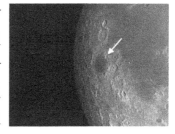

you will see quite a number of small craters, mounds, spots, streaks, and **wrinkle ridges. LTP's** have also been spotted in the region, and some observers have reported being able to see a St. Andrew's Cross emblazoned on the west wall. Grimaldi, in spite of its diameter of 143 miles, is a genuine basin, and if you look closely you might be able to trace out vestiges of an external ring.

Galilaei: [NW/H3] While you're in the neighborhood of Grimaldi, pay your respects to the insignificant little crater Galilaei, about 250 miles north (about four arc-minutes) and reflect upon why the man who opened our eyes to the true nature of the Moon had such an inconsequential feature named after him.

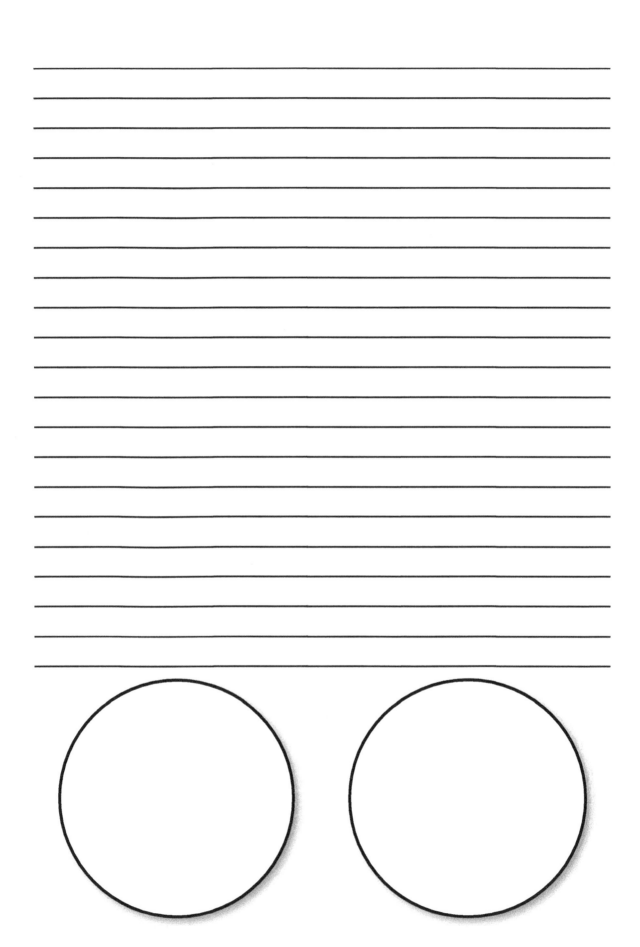

Rimae Sirsalis: [SW/L3-4] Roughly 100 miles southeast of Grimaldi you will see two small overlapping craters, Sirsalis and Sirsalis A (by now you should be able to tell immediately which crater is older). Neighboring these two craters to the east and south is a complex

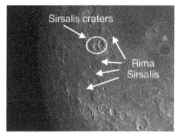

of rilles. Rima Sirsalis is the most conspicuous, but it has lots of neighboring offshoots. How many can you see?

With your telescope at its highest usable power, trace Rima Sirsalis through its full length. Along the way, try to discern the many smaller rilles that branch off. These require larger apertures and good seeing, but it's worth the effort.

Rima Sirsalis is a gift to amateur astronomers because it can be easily seen in the smallest of telescopes. At 240 miles long and two miles wide, it is one of the longest rilles on the Moon, and it reveals itself just before Full Moon—a time when most astronomers are putting their telescopes away!

The experts haven't quite decided what kind of rille Sirsalis is. Some say it is a collapsed lava tube (but why would a lava tube, which forms around meandering lava flows, be so straight?) Others say it is a graben, terrain that has fallen between two parallel fault lines that have pulled apart. What do you think?

Rima Sirsalis is unusual not only because of its great length, but because it cuts straight through a highland region and is rarely persuaded to deviate from its course. The rille begins just east of the crater Darwin, then proceeds north where it "empties" into Oceanus Procellarum. Spend a lot of time here. Draw the network of rilles and keep coming back to improve on what you think you saw.

Schickard: [SW/P4] When you look at Schickard you should immediately notice something unusual: Schickard's floor has stripes! It is dark on both the north and south ends, but there is a wide central stripe of lighter material. You are looking at terrain that is made

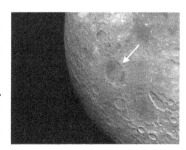

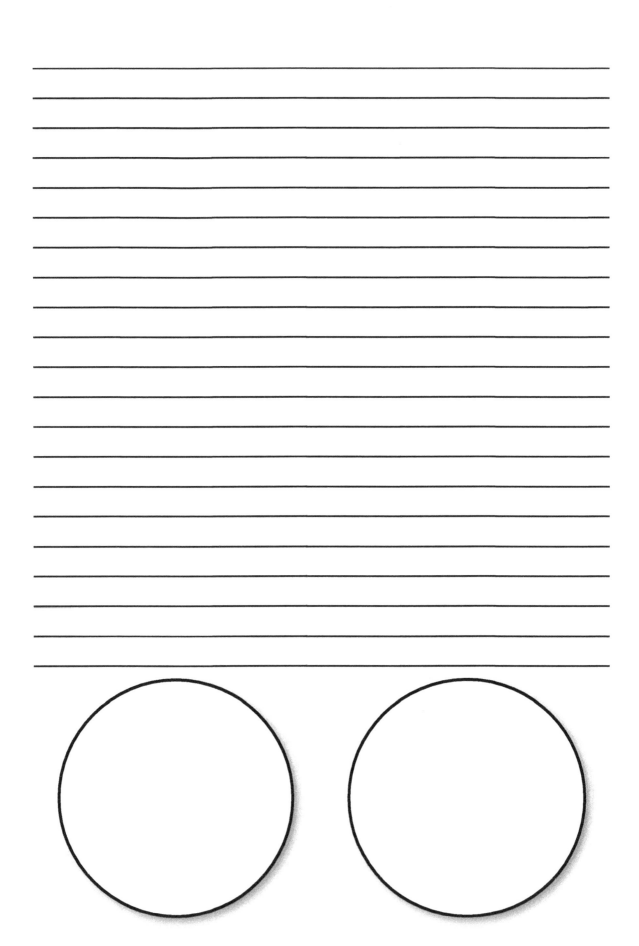

up of two different chemical compositions and is a result of a combination of lighter highland material that was blown in from the formation of the Mare Orientale basin and dark basaltic material (molten lava that welled up from underneath) on the northern and southern portions of Schickard.

D A Y 12

Wargentin: [SW/P4] (Depending on libration, you may have to wait until tomorrow night to see Wargentin.) This is one of the more unusual craters on the Moon. When you catch Wargentin in the right light, it has a fascinating story to tell. There is an almost inviolable

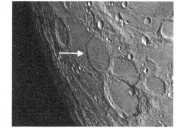

rule that crater floors must be lower than their surrounding terrain. Not so with Wargentin! Unlike most crater impacts that leave obvious depressions, the projectile that created Wargentin blasted out a large hole, then opened up cracks that pierced through to the molten zone far below. Subsequently, hot lava rose through these fissures, filled Wargentin's empty bowl to the brim, then inexplicably stopped just before spilling over!

If the Sun is at a low enough angle, the wrinkle ridge pattern on the surface of Wargentin looks as if an enormous chicken stamped its foot on the ground and flew off just as the lava congealed, leaving its imprint to tantalize the imagination of future astronomers.

Nasmyth/Phocylides: [SW/P-Q4] While you're in the neighborhood of Wargentin, take a look at its two neighbors to the south, Nasmyth and Phocylides. Under the right lighting conditions they look remarkably like a boot print (probably in hot pursuit of the chicken that just flew off from Wargentin).

Day 13 (T=67° W)

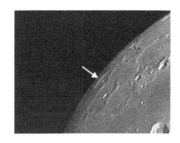

D A Y 13

Pythagoras:† [NW/C3] There is only a brief period during each lunation when Pythagoras is visible. It is a complex crater with two central mountain peaks, terraced walls, and internal features. It is an impressive 80 miles in diameter (compare to Copernicus at 58 miles.) It's spectacular rim mountains rise to an imposing three miles above its floor![43] The central mountain peaks alone attain a height of one mile. Although it is close to the northwest limb and is substantially fore-shortened, it is worth a visit. Try to catch it when the libration is favorable.

Seleucus:† [NW/G3] Seleucus is an admirable little 27-mile crater sitting by itself on the Procellarum lava plains west of Aristarchus and Herodotus. It has a central bump aspiring to be a mountain, a sharply defined ejecta blanket, and terraced walls that rise to more than 10,000 feet.

Struve/Russel: [NW/G2] Close to the west limb you will find an oblong forma-tion that is the result of two overlapping craters which have melted together, Struve and Russel (of Hertzsprung-Russel fame). The fact that there is no hint of a dividing wall is a curiosity. Can you see indications that within the confines of Struve/Russel the lunar surface is curved?

Cardanus: [NW/H2] Just inland from the western shore of Oceanus Procellarum is a pair of craters lined up on a north-south meridian, Cardanus and Kraft. Car-danus, the southernmost, is a prominent 30-mile crater with terraced walls, a

---

[43] To put this into perspective, these peaks would soar 7,000 feet higher than Colorado's 14ers!

central hill, and several small craters on its floor. Of more important interest is the fact that it is linked to Kraft, its neighbor to the north, by a crater chain (called a *catena*) almost 40 miles long. See if you can make out this very thin line of craters.

Reiner Gamma: [Repeated from Day 12—NW/J4] Lunar swirls are absolutely flat features that cast no shadows but leave enigmatic whorl-like markings on the lunar surface. No known geological process could have created them, and to heighten the mystery, instruments on Apollo spacecraft measured strong magnetic fields

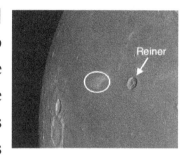

directly over the swirls. For the fanciful, they are eerily reminiscent of crop circles. Of the three swirls on the Moon, two have been found to be **antipodal** features of major impact zones and **mascons**. All three of the swirls on the Moon (there are two on the far side) are associated with strong magnetic anomalies.

Riccioli:† [NW/K2] Because this crater is close to the western limb of the Moon, it's best observed during favorable librations. Riccioli is included primarily because of its historical significance. It is named after a Jesuit priest who named most of the features on the Moon (including this one for himself).

Bailly: [SW/R3] To observe this crater, it is best to wait for a favorable libration. It is a pity that Bailly lies so close to the western limb. It is the largest crater on our side of the Moon and at just under 200 miles it should qualify as a basin. It has ridges, internal craters, and a hint of some multi-ring features. Because its floor has

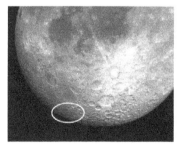

not been flooded by lava, it retains much of the original detail from the moment of its creation. At more than three billion years of age, it's a bit tired and worn down but worth visiting.

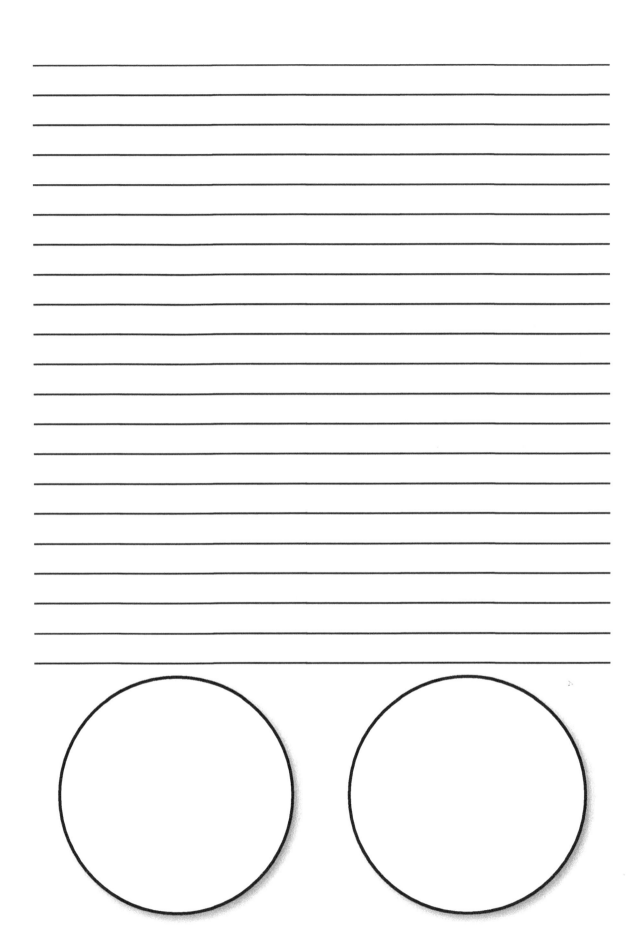

Schickard: [Repeated from Day 12—SW/P4] When you look at Schickard you should immediately notice something unusual: Schickard's floor has stripes! It is dark on both the north and south ends, but there is a wide central stripe of lighter material. You are looking at terrain that is made up of two different chemical

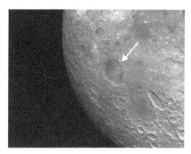

compositions and is a result of a combination of lighter highland material that was blown in from the formation of the Mare Orientale basin and dark basaltic material (molten lava that welled up from underneath) on the northern and southern portions of Schickard.

Wargentin: [Repeated from Day 12—SW/P4] This is one of the more unusual craters on the Moon. When you catch Wargentin in the right light, it has a fascinating story to tell. There is an almost inviolable rule that crater floors must be lower than their surrounding terrain. Not so with Wargentin! Unlike most

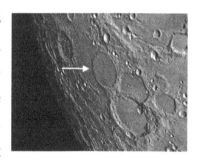

crater impacts that leave obvious depressions, the projectile that created Wargentin blasted out a large hole, then opened up cracks that pierced through to the molten zone far below. Subsequently, hot lava rose through these fissures, filled Wargentin's empty bowl to the brim, then inexplicably stopped just before spilling over!

If the Sun is at a low enough angle, the **wrinkle ridge** pattern on the surface of Wargentin looks as if an enormous chicken stamped its foot on the ground and flew off just as the lava congealed, leaving its imprint to tantalize the imagination of future astronomers.

Mare Orientale/Cordillera Mountains: [SW/L-M libration zone] It is a pity that we are deprived of a decent view of Mare Orientale; it is the Moon's greatest and most pristine example of a multi-ring impact basin.[44] But count your blessings; the tradeoff for a permanent view of the far side would leave us worse off. It would be like staring at vast, unbroken stretches of the Southern Highlands.

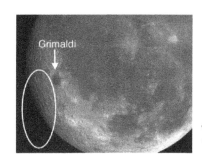

Mare Oriental, however, does shyly reveal herself, if only in part, when **libration** is favorable. At such times you can glimpse its outer ring, the Cordillera Mountains, and sometimes even its inner ring, the Rook Mountains.

_____

_____

_____

_____

_____

_____

_____

_____

_____

_____

_____

_____

_____

_____

---

[44] *Pristine* because it is the youngest and freshest of the great basins. 3.85 billion years does qualify it as "young and fresh," doesn't it?

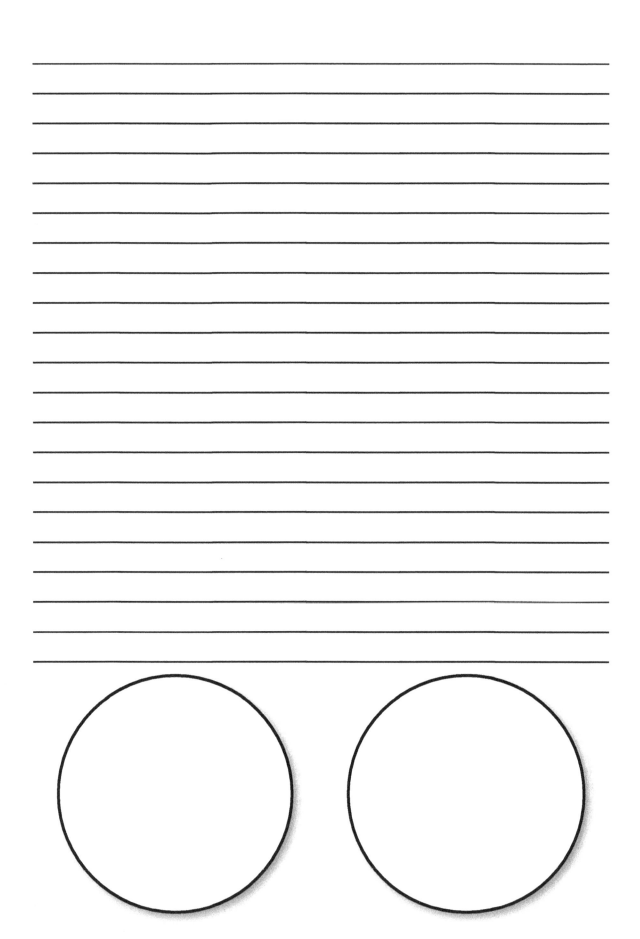

Day 14 (T=81° W)

D
A
Y

14

Full Moon generally occurs around the end of Day 14, but this can vary by up to 12 hours, so Full Moon may happen on Day 15 (also see *Super Moon* in the *Glossary*). To be strictly technical, we never actually see a Full Moon. Such an object must be exactly opposite the Sun from the Earth; it would therefore be in the Earth's shadow and we would be in the grips of a lunar eclipse. What we call a Full Moon must, of necessity, be placed above or below the Earth's shadow (making it slightly less than full). The result is that some craters will always show a bit of shadow relief. Take a look at the Moon now and decide whether it is sailing above or below the Earth's shadow. Pay particular attention to the south polar region and see if you can spot the peaks of the very high Leibnitz Mountains sparkling against the black sky beyond. One of its peaks, Leibnitz β, is the highest mountain on the Moon and at 36,000 feet would tower above Everest!

The most eye-catching features of the Full Moon are the systems of rays surrounding Tycho, Copernicus, and Kepler. Take a look at the "straits" between Mare Imbrium and Oceanus Procellarum. Can you see that the color of the lava in both areas is different? This is a clear indication that the lava flows came from different sources at different times. Also notice the darker ring surrounding Mare Serenitatis, particularly along the eastern and southern shores. It is more conspicuous now that we are at Full Moon. After the Serenity Basin formed, it was covered by darker titanium-rich lava that also caused the basin to sink and open up arcuate cracks along the southern shore. A second, lighter colored lava flow appeared much later, but because this flow did not completely cover the floor of Serenity it left the mare with a dark collar.

Aristillus: [NE/F10] We were first introduced to Aristillus on Day 7 when its more complex features (ramparts, central mountain peaks, terraces, etc.) were conspicuous because of the low sun angle. We can now see that Aristillus is also at the center of a ray system, which means that the crater is less than a billion years old—a mere youngster in lunar terms!

Proclus: [NE/H14] Proclus is a small crater located just west of Mare Crisium. In spite of its size it is one of the brightest spots on the Moon. When you view it around Full Moon you will notice it also has a system of rays that delicately fan out in a telltale butterfly-wing pattern that conveys important information about the flight path of the

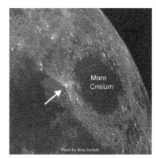

incoming projectile. Proclus is one of the best examples of what happens during a low-angle impact. (See *ejecta patterns* in the *Glossary*.)

Dionysius: [NE/J11] This is a small 11-mile crater on the western shore of Tranquillity, just south of the Ariadaeus Rille. Do you see anything unusual about it? [45]

Linné: [NE/G11] Now that we are at Full Moon, let's re-visit Linné (from Day 6). The light material that surrounds Linné will be very bright tonight. This small 1.5-mile crater has now expanded into about a 6-mile white spot, and because its appearance changes so much with different angles of illumination this was once taken as evidence that the Moon was not a totally dead place.

In 1866 it was erroneously reported that Linné had disappeared. The idea caught on and was cited as proof that the Moon was still geologically active. Observe Linné under different lighting angles and see if you can convince yourself (if you didn't know better) that Linné could disappear.

---

[45] In contrast to Copernicus and Tycho, its rays are dark!

Plinius: [NE/H12] Although the lavas covering Serenity have a brighter hue, can you see that the lava plains of Mare Tranquillitatis are darker and older? The coloring becomes suddenly lighter just north of Plinius and extends, most noticeably, around the eastern shore of Serenity.

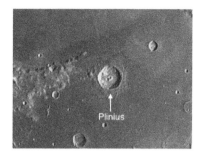

D A Y 14

Furnerius A: [SE/N15] Furnerius A is only 7 miles in diameter but produces a ray that extends for 1,200 miles! How is it that such a tiny crater can splash its debris over nearly half of the Moon's surface! Tonight the entire length of the ray should be clearly visible. (Look closely on the *Field Map* for the tiny arrow that points out Furnerius A, it's easy to miss.)

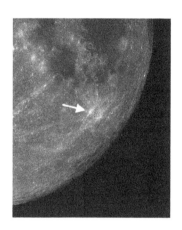

Archimedes:† [NW/G9] Around Full Moon Archimedes will sometimes display, however faintly, a series of bands running across its floor from southwest to northeast. Look closely and you might be able to see that the bands continue unbroken up the NE crater rim and onto the Imbrium floor beyond.

Copernicus: [NW/J7] We first encountered Copernicus, in all of its glory, on Day 9. Most of its conspicuous features have now been washed out by the light of the Full Moon; however, its ray system has become very prominent. Because the impact that created Copernicus excavated down to the lighter highland material that had been

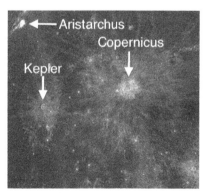

covered over by dark lava, there is a distinct system of whitish rays, second only to those of Tycho, which surrounds the crater and becomes more obvious

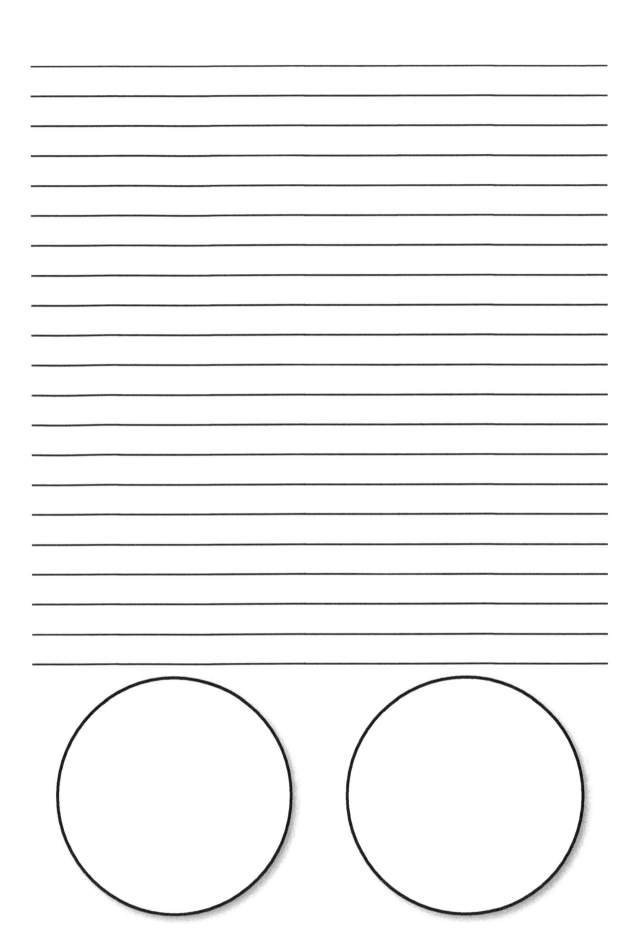

as we approach the Full Moon. Notice how the rays of Copernicus reach out and intertwine with those of Kepler to its west.

A curious feature about the Copernican ray system is that some of the rays do not lead back to the center of the crater; they are, in fact, tangential to it. What ballistic fluke happened in the immediate aftermath of the explosion to have sent the debris on such a bizarre flight path? Notice that there is one ray emanating from the southwest edge of Tycho that exhibits the same peculiar behavior and is even more noticeable.

Aristarchus:† [NW/G5] Aristarchus is the brightest spot on the Moon, a phenomenon that you observed on Day 3 when you noticed that you could see it even on the dark portion of the Moon! It is so bright that Sir William Herschel mistook it for an erupting volcano.[46] On Day 11 did you see, and try to draw, the dark radial bands that climb straight up the west wall of Aristarchus? How many did you see? Some observers have reported up to nine bands. Tonight try to add to the number. Did the bands become more or less prominent as the Sun rose higher since Day 11? Did they creep up the wall and spill over onto the lunar terrain beyond?

Kepler:† [NW/J6] We first visited Kepler on Day 10. Now take a look at it under the Full Moon to appreciate how its rays intertwine with those of Copernicus and Aristarchus. Notice how Kepler's longest western ray points directly to Reiner Gamma (below), the most famous of the enigmatic lunar **swirls**. It has been suggested, somewhat mysteriously, that this is more than a coincidence.

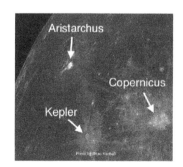

---

[46] William Herschel: 18th c. English astronomer who discovered Uranus.

Reiner Gamma: [Repeated from Day 12—NW/J4] Lunar swirls are absolutely flat features that cast no shadows but leave interesting whorl-like markings on the lunar surface. No known geological process could have created them, and to heighten the mystery, instruments on Apollo spacecraft measured strong

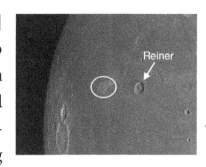

magnetic fields directly over the swirls. For the fanciful, they are eerily reminiscent of crop circles. Of the three swirls on the Moon, two have been found to be antipodal features of major impact zones and mascons. All of the swirls on the Moon (there are two on the far side) are associated with strong magnetic anomalies. When the Kepler rays become visible, notice how Kepler's longest western ray points directly to Reiner Gamma.

Pytheas secondary craters: [NW/G7-8] The best place to see secondary craters that have landed within a splash ray is just 25 miles east of Pytheas. On Day 9 you saw an alignment of seven or more secondary craters that were pointing back to Copernicus, 160 miles to the south. Tonight the craters have disap-

peared due to the high Sun elevation, but the ray can be more clearly seen. If you drew the alignment of craters on Day 9, fill in the splash ray around them tonight.

Alphonsus: [SW/L9] We last observed Alphonsus on Day 7 where we learned about pyroclastic eruptions. The dark halos resulting from these eruptions should still be clearly visible on the floor of Alphonsus, although other features of the crater disappear under the Full Moon.

Tycho: [SW/P8] On Day 8 we got to see Tycho in its persona as the prototype of **complex craters**. Now we get to see its other face: it has the most spectacular system of rays on the Moon, and on Day 14 they blossom into their full glory.

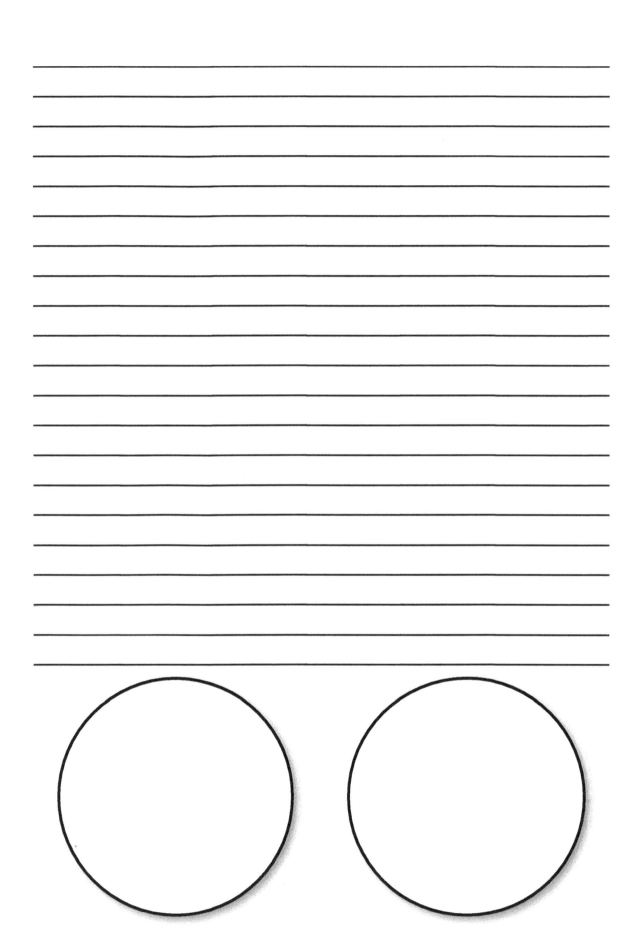

As you gaze at the ray system, try to appreciate the force behind an impact that would scatter boulders more than a thousand miles across the surface of the Moon. It is popularly assumed that these rays have the texture of face powder and that an astronaut would have difficulty detecting them if he were standing in the middle. Such is not the case. The brighter rays are made up of ejected rubble that consists of crushed rock and boulders that are up to a couple of feet in diameter. Large rays are commonly several feet thick and would be difficult to walk through.

With one curious exception, all the rays converge, quite logically, on Tycho, their point of origin. But there is one ray extending from the SW portion of Tycho's nimbus (the dark collar that just encircles the rim) that does not lead us directly back to Tycho; it is actually tangential to it! Copernicus has some similarly curious rays. What ballistic fluke happened in the immediate aftermath of the explosion to have sent the debris on such a bizarre flight path?

The Tycho ray pattern gives us important information. Notice how the rays are not equally distributed in all directions but fly off toward the northwest, east, and southwest; however, there is a large empty zone toward the west (called "the forbidden zone"). This is where the impactor came from. This butterfly pattern is indicative of a very low-flying object, otherwise the rays would be distributed equally around the impact point, as they are with Copernicus and Kepler (both of which you can see very clearly tonight). The exact same process that created the Tycho rays was duplicated closer to the eastern limb at the craters

The explosion that blew out the Tycho crater has been estimated to be the equivalent of 30 trillion tons of TNT! To put this into perspective, imagine the energy that was released by the Hiroshima bomb. Now try to picture two million of those bombs going off at the same time! (The energy from the meteor impact that destroyed the dinosaurs equaled an incredible 100 trillion tons of TNT!)

Proclus [H14] and Stevinus A and Furnerius A [N15], with nearly identical results. And here is a curious thing: the butterfly patterns around these four craters all indicate that the impactors came in from the west. Coincidence?

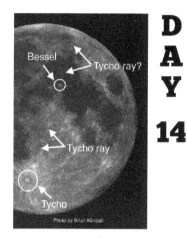

There is one jaw-dropping ray that appears to extend from Tycho all the way across Mare Serenitatis and keeps on going. There has been some speculation that this ray has merely been "renewed" by a ray from the crater Bessel [NE/G11] which it crosses. **Patrick Moore** finds this implausible, and it does seem unlikely that Bessel would produce only *one* solitary ray of such magnificence.

Tycho has another unusual feature that is brought out by the high Sun: Notice the nimbus, the dark collar that just encircles the rim. No other crater on the Moon has a surrounding nimbus that is so dark.

At a mere 109 million years, Tycho is the youngest of the large craters on the Moon. Although it's northern cousin, Copernicus, is about 800 million years old, they are both considered "youngsters." Notice how the rays emanating from Copernicus and Tycho

Tycho is so young that its nimbus has not had enough time to be pelted into obscurity by ensuing myriads of micro-meteorites. The process, which also removes bright splash rays, takes about a billion years.

have entirely different characters. Whereas the Tycho rays are clearly delineated, those from Copernicus are wispy, plume-like, and shorter. It is curious that this is so, particularly since Copernicus is the larger crater and was created by a more powerful explosion.

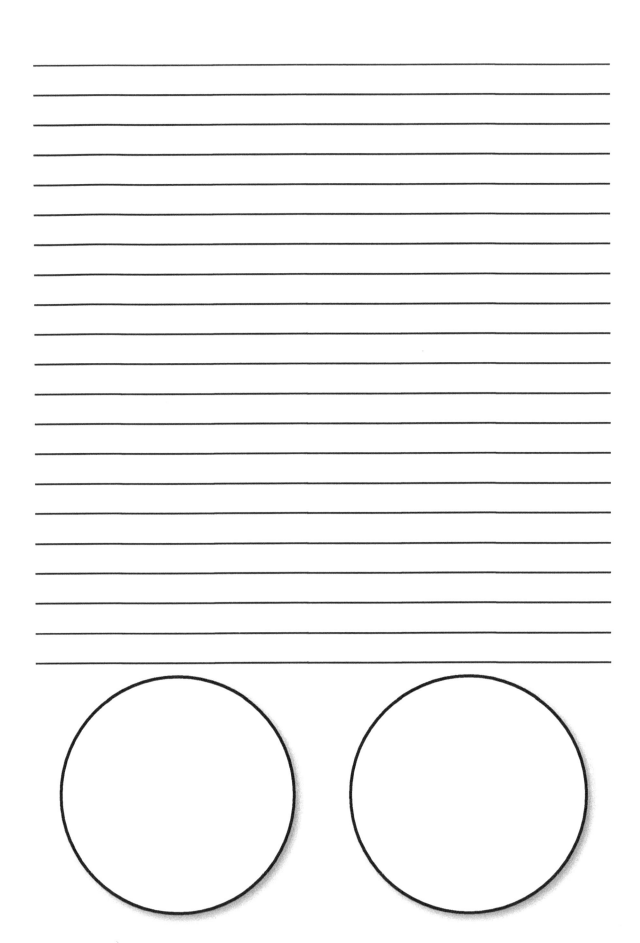

Day 15 and beyond

For observational purposes there is fundamentally no difference between Days 14 and 15—they both look like the Full Moon to the casual observer. From here on out, all the features that we've covered since Day 1 reappear; the only difference is that we will now see these objects at lunar sunset instead of sunrise. As a result, you will see new details appearing that you hadn't noticed before because the sunlight is streaming in from the opposite direction. Asymmetrical formations such as rilles, scarps, and irregular craters in particular will reveal details that weren't visible during the first 14 days. The biggest advantage now is that the Moon will not be so low to the horizon, and objects will not be washed out by atmospheric murk. Because the Moon will not disappear so quickly, you have more time to relax and enjoy crisper views of features that are close to the eastern rim.

Since we are now in "repeat mode," to read about features for a particular day after Full Moon you need to find out which lunar day they were first described on. To do so, subtract 14 from the lunar day after Full Moon that you wish to observe on. For example, if you are on Day 17 of the lunar cycle, subtract 14 from 17 and turn to Day 3 of this *Guide*. (To find the current lunar day, use an app such as *SkySafari Plus, Deluxe Moon Standard,* or *Lunatic*.) Objects for Day 4 can also be profitably observed, but with diminished contrast since they are deeper into the sunlit portion of the Moon.

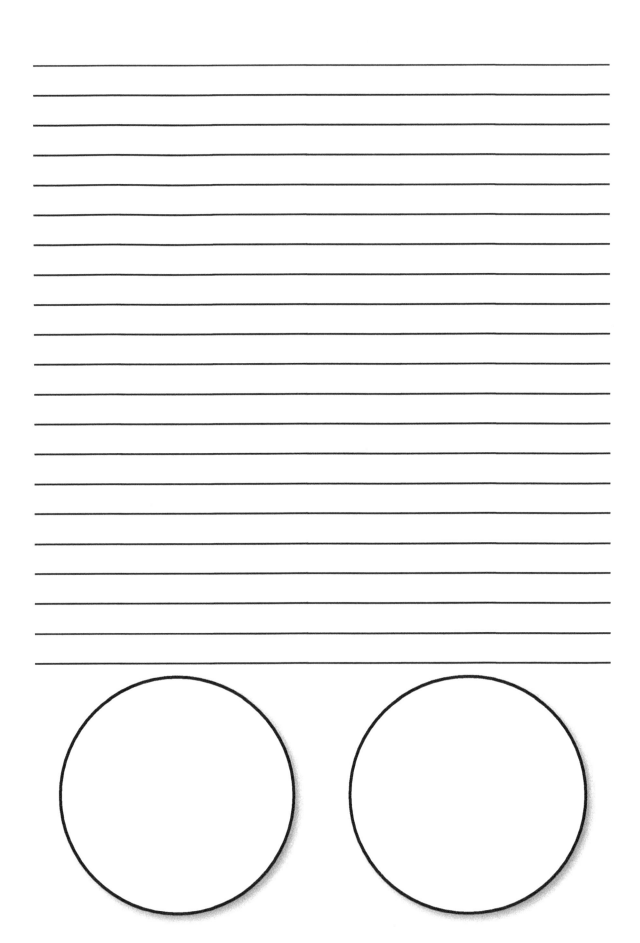

Day 16 (T=72°)

The features on Days 16 and 17 are the same that you observed on Days 3 and 4. However, because of the different lighting they are particularly noteworthy and some look entirely different.

Endymion: [NE/D15] This is an older crater which somewhat resembles Plato [Day 8; NW/D9] in that it has a smooth, dark-chocolate floor and three-mile-high walls which cast lovely shadow spires on the flood plain below when the Sun is low.

Geminus: [NE/F15] Roughly 200 miles north of Mare Crisium (below) you will find the moderately complex 55-mile crater Geminus. It has terraced walls and small central peaks.

200 miles would be about three arc-minutes north of Crisium. Being familiar with the field of view (FOV) of your eyepieces will help you navigate.

Mare Crisium: [NE/H15] On Day 16 you should be able to observe Crisium's complexities more successfully than you did on Day 3, particularly the high eastern mountain border. We tend to think of craters as comparatively small objects and lose sight of the

fact that large lunar "seas" are the result of crater impacts also. Basically, if it's round, it's a crater. Mare Crisium resulted from the impact of a large meteor 3.9 billion years ago. The event was energetic enough to leave a **multi-ring** imprint, parts of which we can clearly see tonight. Notice the ring features bending around Crisium on its north side. Particularly notice how Mare Anguis on the NE side of Crisium [G16] extends itself toward the west, passes below Cleomedes, and then dissipates at Tisserand. The Crisium basin appears elliptical, with its long axis running from north to south. This is an illusion due to the effects of

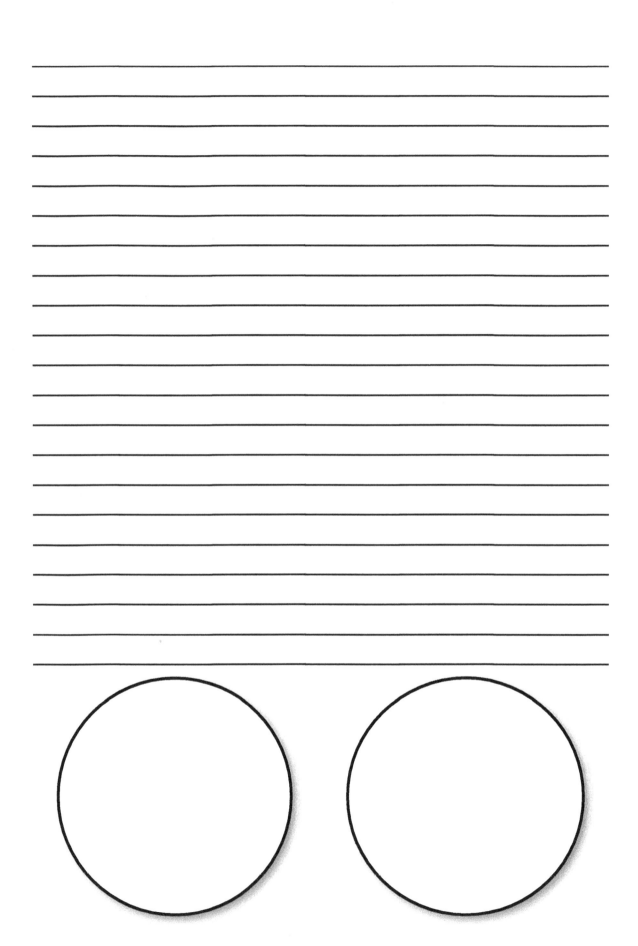

foreshortening. Crisium actually *is* elliptical, but, contrary to what your eyes tell you, its long axis runs east to west.[47]

Once you have become familiar with the details on the surface of Mare Crisium, particularly around Promontorium Agarum [H16], be on the lookout for **LTP's.** These have been reported from time to time and manifest themselves as mists that mysteriously appear and obscure some of the surrounding details.

Promontorium Agarum: [NE/H16] an impressive cape on the SE edge of Crisium. It has peaks that tower several thousand feet above its floor. **LTP's** have occasionally been reported in this region, especially right after sunrise.

The Great Eastern Chain: [SE/K-N16] There is a conspicuous chain of large craters, at one time referred to as the Great Western Chain,[48] which closely hugs the same meridian near the eastern limb (i.e., the rim of the visible disk) of the Moon. They start on the south-eastern shore of the Sea of Fertility (Mare Fecunditatis)

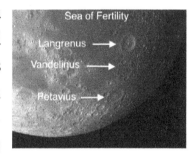

and continue south. The chain consists of Langrenus, Vendelinus, Petavius, and Furnerius. Although this unusual alignment is coincidental, it was once posited as evidence to support the **endogenic theory** of crater formation. Tonight you should be able to see them more clearly than you did on Day 3.

Of the first two craters, Langrenus and Vendelinus, one is older than the other and appeared before the lava flows started. It should be easy for you to decide on their comparative ages.[49] Even if you have a small telescope, there is much detail in the interior and on the outer ramparts to keep you busy.

---

[47] If you have the *Moon Globe HD* app, you can see this for yourself. Do a search for Mare Crisium as it normally appears near the east rim of the Moon. Notice how it is elongated north to south. Now with one finger, rotate Crisium to the center of the Moon and it will develop its true east-west elongation.

[48] In 1961 the IAU reversed the east-west directions on the Moon.

[49] See *Crater Age* in the *Glossary*.

Petavius: [SE/M16] This is one of the most beautiful craters on the Moon. An example of a **floor-fractured crater** (FFC), a type of crater that has been modified by later volcanism, uplift, and consequent fracturing. The floor of Petavius is nearly 1,000 feet higher near its center than around the edge! Is the curvature of the lunar surface apparent on its floor? Turbulence and volcanic upheaval from below split the central mountain (which rises to nearly one mile above the floor) and formed the rilles.

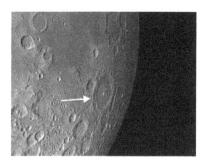

D A Y 16

The principal rille, Rima Petavius, is so prominent that it can be seen with a 60mm refractor. It is a **graben**, an elongated depression that results when stresses open up two parallel cracks in the lunar crust and the terrain in between drops. The rille extends from the central peak to the southwest wall. There is actually a system of rilles on the floor. How many can you see with your instrument?

_____

_____

_____

_____

_____

_____

_____

_____

_____

_____

_____

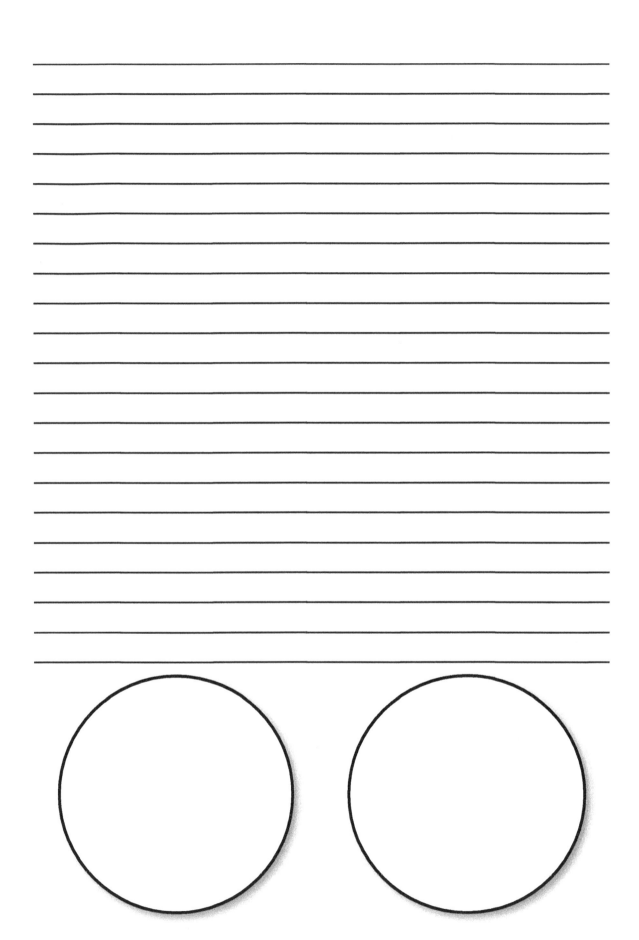

Day 17 (T=60°)

Burckhardt: [NE/F15] This is the crater with the "Mickey Mouse ears." It is a remarkable exception to the rule that when one crater intrudes upon another, the younger crater (the intruder) is always smaller. Burckhardt has landed smack in between two smaller but older craters, giving it the Mickey Mouse effect.

Cleomedes: [NE/G15] Cleomedes is the first significant crater just north of Mare Crisium. It is a splendid 80-mile crater with **terraced walls, rilles**, and a small central mountain. There are also two craterlets, and a y-shaped rille on the northern half of the floor just east of the central mountain peak. Notice that the floor is unusually smooth. Because it sits directly over one of the multi-rings encircling the Crisium basin, it is believed that lava rose up through Crisium fractures and smoothly covered the floor of Cleomedes. Under a low-angle Sun you might be able to detect that the rille cuts through a small dome on the northern section of the floor.

The Flying Eagle: [NE/H15] As the lava cooled following the impact that created Mare Crisium, a series of **wrinkle ridges**, known as Dorsum Oppel, formed along the entire western edge and give the impression of waves lapping on the shore. The flowing lava partially filled the pre-existing craters Yerkes

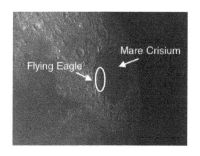

and Lick [H15], turning them into **ghost craters**. There is also a more substantial ridge that connects the flooded crater Yerkes with the smaller Yerkes E, 15 miles to its northwest (unnamed on the *Field Map*). Under a low Sun (when the terminator is around 52°-55°) this ridge looks remarkably like the silhouette of a bird in flight and has been nicknamed the *Flying Eagle*.

Peirce & Picard: [NE/H15] The two largest intact craters on Mare Crisium are Peirce and Picard. They are only about 12 miles in diameter by 1 mile deep and will require 75x-100x to see them. They are located on a more or less north-south line about 30 miles in from the western shore of Crisium (Peirce is the northernmost). The lava that covered Crisium stopped flowing before these craters formed. You should easily be able to spot Swift, a small 7-mile crater just eight miles to the north of Peirce.

D A Y 17

O'Neill's Bridge: [NE/H15] There is a fascinating lesson here about how even trained scientists can allow their imaginations to run away with them. In 1953, amateur astronomer John O'Neill, using a 4" refractor, reported having discovered a man-made bridge near the western shore of Mare Crisium. The bridge "had the amazing span of about 12 miles from pediment to pediment." (The two "pediments" were the tip ends of Promentorium Lavinium and Promentorium Olivium.)[50] O'Neill called for verification from professionals, and British astronomer Hugh Percy Wilkins corroborated that there was, indeed, such a bridge. American astronomers disputed the claim, saying that it was an illusion. But before the matter was settled, the news media prematurely announced the discovery of an artificial bridge on the Moon. (Not coincidentally, the 1950s were the peak of the "flying saucer" rage, so the public was ripe!) Wilkins was blamed for the resulting media circus and was forced to resign from the British Astronomical Association.

Now put yourself to the test! Tonight near the southwest shore of Mare Crisium you will find the ghost crater Yerkes. Immediately west of Yerkes are

---

[50] These two promontories are not listed on the *Field Map*, but they are immediately to the west of the *Flying Eagle* (above).

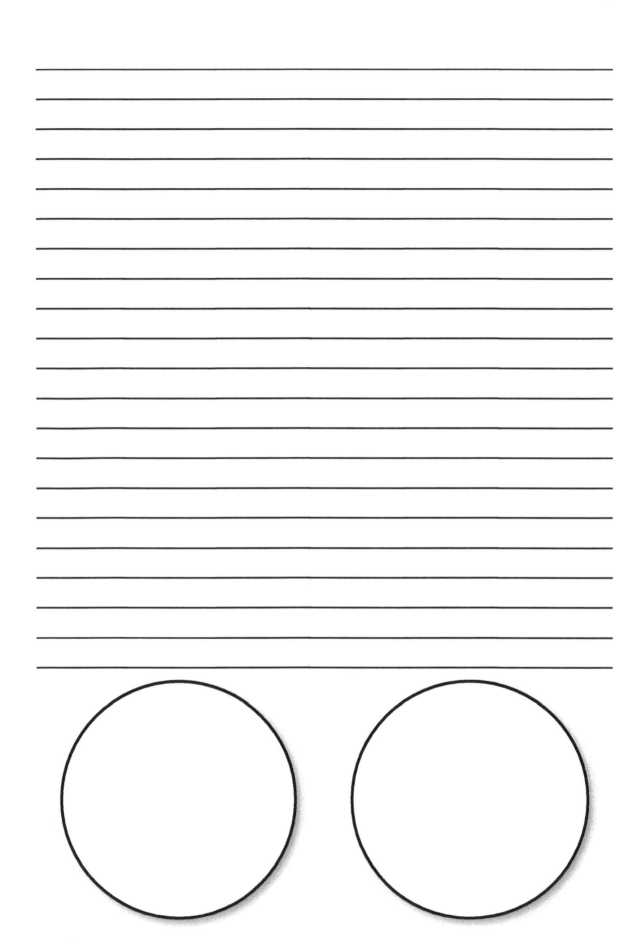

two promontories forming the shoreline of Crisium. When the Sun is at the right angle, the lighting will create the illusion of a bridge spanning the two promontories. Could you be convinced, in a more gullible climate, that you were staring at a man-made bridge? (Wilkins was using a 15" Newtonian at 300x.) The best time to view the bridge is around Day 17 when the **terminator** is near 53° and the two promontories are just lit up by the setting Sun. If you don't see it tonight, keep trying. The lighting has to be perfect.

Furnerius: [SE/N16] This is the last of the craters that make up the *Great Eastern Chain* and it is very old, having formed before the impact that created the Nectaris basin 3.9 billion years ago. Although the walls have been battered down and show their age, there are still many complexities remaining which will

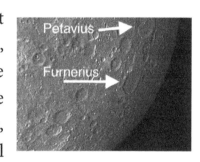

reward careful observation. There are several craterlets of varying sizes on the floor of Furnerius, including a 30-mile rille extending from the north rim toward the southeast. **Patrick Moore** reports that there are fourteen large craters and several craterlets in its interior. (A more reasonable assessment would be there is one large crater and several craterlets.) Make a rough sketch of how many you can see, then come back next month (and on Day 3) to see if you can add to the count. Can you match Patrick Moore's observing skills?

Leibnitz Mountains: [SE/T13] Follow the terminator all the way south and continue a short way beyond the end of the crescent. If you're lucky, you'll see tiny star-like points of light shining in the dark beyond the limb of the Moon. These are the tops of the Leibnitz Mountains, a range so high that at 36,000 feet one of its peaks, Leibnitz β (Beta), the highest mountain on the Moon, would tower above Mt. Everest! Unfortunately the Leibnitz Mountains are not well placed for viewing, but it's worth trying to get a peek at the Moon's highest mountain.

FINAL THOUGHTS

Now that you've become familiar with the most exciting object in the heavens, it's guaranteed that you will start to develop a serious case of "aperture fever" (probably sooner than later) and will want to branch out from the Moon. If you started out with a very small telescope like a 2.4" refractor or a 6" reflector, then the next most logical jump would be to an 8" reflector of some sort.

Avoid department store telescopes and any telescope whose main advertising teaser is the power. Telescopes will generally max out at 50x per inch of diameter, so if you're looking at a 2.4" telescope that boasts 700x run, don't walk, to the nearest exit! (Technically they will supply you with an eyepiece that gives 700x, but the image will be so blurry that it will be unrecognizable!) The most important thing about a telescope is not its magnification but its ability to gather lots of light. Here's where bigger actually is better—assuming that the optics are of high quality. (Don't skimp here. A 6" mirror of high quality will easily outperform a larger mirror that is cheaper but was made poorly.)

The greatest thing to happen to amateur astronomy was the invention of the Dobsonian telescope by John Dobson in the 1960s. John's design eventually allowed amateurs to build or buy very large "light bucket" telescopes at minimal cost that were easily transported to dark skies and simple to set up and use. The larger mirrors allowed astronomers to see faint objects such as galaxies, nebulas, and star clusters that only professionals could see a few years before. The "Dobsonian revolution" didn't begin in earnest until the 1980s. (In 1969, *Sky and Telescope* magazine rejected his ideas as being beneath their standards!)

My recommendation for your next step is to get an 8" or 10" Dobsonian. There is a learning curve involved as you must be able to find your way around the sky by "star hopping"—but that's fun and will give you an intimate knowledge of the constellations. Two good books to introduce you to star hopping are *Star-Hopping for Backyard Astronomers* by Alan M. MacRobert and *Star-Hopping: Your Visa to Viewing the Universe* by Robert A. Garfinkle. And for a general interest introduction to astronomy, you can't do better than *Night Watch* by Terence Dickinson. It is now in its fourth edition and has been the top-selling stargazing guide in the world for the last 20 years.

Don't be intimidated by the prospect of learning how to star hop. The entire night sky will be at your disposal and you'll have bragging rights to being a "real astronomer." But because of busy schedules and work commitments, that may not be possible, so a second-best recommendation (albeit a more expensive one) is to get an 8" SCT (Schmidt Cassegrain Telescope) from either Celestron or Orion. These are small, portable "go to" telescopes that will automatically find thousands of objects for you. All you have to do is push a button.

You have now been launched onto one of the most rewarding journeys imaginable. May you enjoy clear skies and many nights discovering the endless secrets of the universe!

GLOSSARY

The following section is a great deal more than just a *Glossary*. It contains much ancillary information that is, nevertheless, critical for astronomers to understand. As such, it would be a rewarding cloudy night activity to sit down and read through this section.

albedo: the fraction of sunlight that is reflected off an object. Albedo numbers are between 0.00 (the darkest) and 1.00 (the whitest). The Moon has a surprisingly low albedo of 0.07, meaning it reflects only 7% of the sunlight that falls on its surface. Considering how bright the Full Moon is, this is, unbelievably, a little darker than asphalt! The crater Aristarchus [G5] has the highest albedo on the Moon (0.18), Grimaldi [K3] has the lowest (0.04). For comparison, albedo numbers for other objects are…

- perfectly white body: 1.0
- fresh snow: 0.8
- grass: 0.23
- aged asphalt: 0.10
- coal: 0.05
- perfectly black body: 0.00

angular diameter: the angle that an object subtends at the eye of the observer. The Moon, at an average distance of about 240,000 miles, subtends an angle of 31.7 arc-minutes. But because the Moon travels in an ellipse, not a circle, this will vary from 29.7 arc-minutes at apogee to 33.9 arc-minutes at perigee. Therefore, the angle that one mile subtends on the Moon will vary slightly from 0.83 arc-seconds to 0.94 arc-seconds (discounting the effects of foreshortening for objects near the limbs). At the average distance of the Moon this equals 0.89

arc-seconds per mile. This figure is handy when you're trying to figure out how small a crater you are able to perceive with your telescope.

antipodal: diametrically opposed; appearing on the opposite side of the Moon (or any globe).

Antoniadi Seeing Scale: (also see *Pickering Seeing Scale*) A clear night does not guarantee that you will see objects clearly through your telescope. Sometimes, even when there's not a cloud in the sky, the atmosphere is so turbulent that detail is totally washed out. The Antoniadi Seeing Scale allows you to quantify the seeing conditions of planets and the Moon. It ranks the quality of seeing from I to V. Look at a large, complex crater or a planet such as Jupiter or Saturn and apply the following scale:

I: Excellent seeing, without a quiver. Image sharp and quite steady, even when high power is used.

II: Slight quivering of the image with moments of calm lasting several seconds.

III: Fair. Frequent unsteady periods, but good seeing in the steady intervals.

IV: Poor. Constant troublesome undulations of the image.

V: Very poor. Unsharp image even with low power.

apogee: the point at which the Moon is farthest away from the Earth in its elliptical orbit.

arc-minute: A unit of angular measure, equivalent to one-sixtieth of a degree.

arc-second: The 60th part of a minute. This is pretty small stuff—a pinhead at 100 yards covers one arc-second. One mile at the median distance of the Moon rather conveniently **subtends** an angle of about one arc-second (0.89 arc-seconds, to be precise).[51] A 5-inch telescope with good optics should resolve one arc-second.

banded craters: A few craters show distinct banding when they are in sunlight. This could be produced by small landslides or lava flows that have channeled over the crater's rim, or the bands may simply reflect natural variations in the composition of the lunar crust. Aristarchus [NW/G5] is the most conspicuous example, but Manilius [NE/H10] also has bands worth exploring.

barycenter: the center of mass (rather like a "point of balance") between two systems that are revolving around each other. The barycenter of the Earth-Moon system is located about 1,000 miles below the Earth's surface. Because of this, many scientists consider that the Earth and Moon are not a true "double planet," as they would be if the barycenter were located in space.[52]

basins: (see crater *morphology: basin*)

butterfly pattern: a system of splash rays that delicately fan out around a crater indicating that the impactor was a very low-flying object; otherwise the rays would be distributed equally around the impact point, as they are with Copernicus [NW/H8] and Kepler [NW/J6]. Tycho [SW/P8] and Proclus [NE/H14] are the best examples of a butterfly pattern.

bya: billion years ago

Caldwell Catalog: (see *Moore, Patrick*)

---

[51] This is at the center of the Moon or, closer to the east or west limbs, along the lines of longitude only. Away from the center you must take foreshortening into account. At perigee and apogee these figures will change slightly.

[52] The Moon is actually larger than Pluto which, with its moon Charon, used to be considered a double planet, and will be considered so once again as soon as the International Astronomical Union comes to its senses and restores Pluto to its former status as a real planet.

catena: Crater chain—a series of small craters in a compact line. Crater chains can be formed when a comet or asteroid is torn into pieces by the gravitational pull of a large body like the Earth or the Moon. The smaller pieces, which are stretched out into a line as they fly through space, then slam into the Moon in machine-gun fashion, leaving a straight trail of small craters. The possibility of such an event was once a controversial idea, but in 1994 Comet Shoemaker-Levy silenced the critics when it slammed into Jupiter leaving the very same type of markings.[53] The Moon's best example is Catena Davy (Day 5).

celestial equator: The great circle on the celestial sphere that lies directly above the equator of the Earth. Its position slowly moves due to **precession**.

central mountain peaks: Craters that are larger than 10-12 miles in diameter form central mountain peaks (which will start out as low hills) then become quite magnificent in larger *Tycho-class* craters. These central mountains are created when an object slams into the Moon and compresses the terrain underneath. This material then rebounds to form magnificent peaks. Scientists are not sure why some "central" mountain peaks are off-center. One possibility is that they are the result of oblique impacts. (Scientific experiments have verified that, contrary to logic, oblique impacts leave the resulting craters perfectly round unless the impactor came in at an extremely low angle.)

colongitude: (see *selenographic colongitude*)

complex crater: (see *crater morphology*)

compression phase: (see *crater formation*)

---

[53] The encounter between Jupiter and comet Shoemaker-Levy released a mind-boggling 20 million megatons of energy (this would equal more than 30 billion Hiroshima bombs!)

concentric craters: There are several craters on the Moon that have inner rings that curiously make them look a bit like donuts, they seem so perfectly cut out. For a time it was thought that these were craters that had received dead-center impacts from smaller meteorites, but that theory has now been called into doubt. Wood once catalogued 51 such craters and found two important common denominators: All had diameters of between 1.2 and 12 miles, and most of them occurred near the edges of lunar seas. "The inner donuts," he concluded, "cannot be impacts that just happened to be centered on pre-existing craters." (Alas, another bubble burst!) Hesiodus A [SW/M8] and Marth [SW/N7] are the Moon's best examples of concentric craters. (Is it just a coincidence they are both located on the southern shore of Mare Nubium?)

crater: A bowl-shaped depression on the surface of the Moon left by the impact of a comet, asteroid, or meteor. Craters justifiably get the best press and are quite stunning when viewed through even the smallest telescopes. Some 10,000 craters larger than two miles in diameter are visible through amateur telescopes with at least a 6" aperture. (For a description of the various crater types and sizes, see **Crater Morphology**.) The most conspicuous craters are named after philosophers, mathematicians, and scientists, such as Copernicus, Kepler, Plato, Aristoteles, and Pythagoras.

crater age: There are several benchmarks you can use to decide on a crater's age:

1. **Esthetic appeal:** A dependable (albeit highly subjective) indication that one crater is younger than another is the fact that it is more interesting to look at. Over time, subsequent meteorite impacts and erosion from the effects of solar wind will wear down and cover up features that once gave a crater some personality. So basically, if it's boring, it's old. Craters with strong esthetic appeal like Tycho and Copernicus, which exhibit steep sides, central mountain peaks, stair-step terraces and ejecta blankets, are comparatively young.

2. **Size:** Crater size is a reasonably good indication of its age. With few exceptions, if a crater is small, it's young.

3. **Crater overlap:** This is a dead giveaway. Young craters will overlap older craters and, with remarkable consistency, will be smaller than the craters they intrude upon. This is true even when craters have appeared within a relatively short time of each other. Good examples are Janssen [SE/P13], Albategnius [SE/L10], Stöfler [SE/P10], and Thebit [SW/M9]. The Moon offers surprisingly few exceptions to this rule, e.g., Burckhardt [Day 3; NE/F15], Aristoteles (Day 6; NE/D11], Longomontanus [Day 8; SW/P7], and Russel [Day 13; NW/G2].

4. **Brightness of ejecta pattern:** When an impactor slams against the Moon, particularly on the **maria**, it excavates brighter material from greater depths and spreads it across the dark lava flows on the surface. Subsequent micrometeorite and solar wind bombardment will gradually darken this material to blend in with the surrounding terrain, but the process takes about a billion years or so.

crater-diameter: Often used as a term of comparative distance. For example, "three crater-diameters to the southwest of Archimedes" means to notice the diameter of Archimedes and then move your telescope to the southwest a distance equivalent to three craters the size of Archimedes.

crater formation: Virtually all craters are the result of impacts from meteorites, asteroids, and comets slamming into the Moon at high speeds.[54] The impactors will typically excavate craters that are 10-20 times the size of the original projectile. Some 10,000 craters larger than two miles in diameter are visible through amateur telescopes with at least a 6" aperture—enough to keep you busy for a long time!

---

[54] See *exogenic/endogenic* for conflicting theories.

(There are also 230 craters with diameters larger than 60 miles. These can be seen with ordinary binoculars.)

There are three phases of crater formation: compression, ejection, and modification. The compression and ejection phases happen virtually instantaneously. During the compression phase a projectile slams into the Moon and transfers an enormous amount of kinetic energy downward into the lunar rock and soil, which become highly compressed (think of a very large, very powerful spring). The ejection phase begins less than 1/100 of a second later when the compressed rock rebounds and explodes upwards, widening a hole in the lunar surface that is typically 10 times larger than the size of the original impactor. How wide the hole is, and its resulting morphology, depend on the size and speed of the offending projectile.

Surprisingly, the ejection phase can last up to several minutes, so during the late heavy bombardment period the Moon must have looked like a lunar version of Yellowstone National Park with geysers of molten rock spewing out at intervals.

The modification phase begins after the fireworks have stopped, but you still don't want to be standing in the way. With **simple craters**, modification is just a matter of boulders rolling down the sides of the bowl and slightly flattening the bottom. As craters increase in size, things start to become dramatic. Large segments of the crater's steep wall will often slump to form stair-step terraces that are clearly visible through backyard telescopes. If the crater is full of molten rock when parts of its wall collapse, a tidal wave of lava can be raised that will race to the opposite side, slam into the wall, and spill over to the lunar terrain beyond, leaving a smooth veneer of impact melt. (See *Theophilus, Day 5*.)

crater morphology: Morphology here refers to the study of the form and structure of craters on the Moon. Craters have three distinctly separate parts which you should focus your attention on as you are observing: the outer slopes, the inner wall, and the floor.

The different morphological characteristics that craters exhibit are solely a function of their diameters. Craters fall into three basic categories: *simple, complex,* and *basin* (referred to as the main sequence). As you are observing craters, decide which of these three categories they belong to.

simple: There are more simple craters on the Moon than any other type. They are usually less than ten miles in diameter. Simple craters start out with the shape of a round bowl with smooth, circular rims, e.g., Moltke, [SE/K12]. However, some of them develop flat floors resulting from a cascade of boulders which have rolled down the interior walls and settled at the bottom. (Lalande A, Mösting A [SW/K9]).

With patience, good lighting and decent optics, you should be able to tell if a simple crater has a flat or rounded floor by looking at the shadow of the rim as it crosses the center of the floor. The shadow on a bowl-shaped floor will appear as a smooth arc; the shadow falling across a flat floor will be truncated, i.e., the apex will be squared off.[55]

complex: As the energy of the impact increases, craters go from smooth bowls to magnificent complex affairs with terraced walls, central mountain peaks, flat floors, and ejecta blankets. In short, they develop personality! This process begins when their diameters exceed 10 to 12 miles. Their rims lose the smooth bowl-like appearance of simple craters and often become scalloped and irregular. There are two types of complex craters: the Triesnecker style and the Tycho style.

Triesnecker [NE/J10] is an illustration of the beginning stage of complex crater morphology. It has a burgeoning central peak (which may be nothing more than a scattering of small hills) and a wreath of material encircling the floor that has slumped down from the rim.

---

[55] Simple craters are also useful objects for testing both the quality of your optics and the seeing conditions. The *Field Map* conveniently lists the diameters of all craters on the reverse side. Look for craters that are less than 9 mi. in diameter, then use the **Virtual Moon Atlas** program to find the days they are visible.

From Triesnecker-class craters we move up to a type of complex crater that is truly magnificent: the **Tycho-class**.[56] These craters are splendid creations with complex central mountain peaks, flat floors, ejecta blankets, and palatial stair-step terraces resulting from enormous landslides.[57] Central mountain peaks, which formed during the ejection phase of crater formation, are the result of the rebound of underlying rocks that were compressed by the force of the original impact.

basins: Do not lose sight of the fact that basins, as large and impressive as they are, are still impact craters and take their place on a continuum from something pretty small (simple craters) to something pretty big (the large dark areas on the Moon called seas, such as Mare Imbrium). They are, in fact, the very largest of craters and are fascinating objects to explore.

When a crater attains a diameter of about 200 miles or greater, its morphology changes once again (although the transition is not so neat and tidy as it is when we are going from simple to complex craters). The most significant characteristic of basins is that at the time of impact a series of outwardly expanding rings are created (in much the same way that a rock dropped into a pond produces concentric ripples). Moon observers have a significant advantage, however. The expanding ripples have become frozen into place and we can observe them (or their fragments) through backyard telescopes billions of years later!

Example: Altai Scarp (Days 5 and 18). The magnificent mountain ranges of the lunar Alps, the Caucasus, the Apennines, and the Carpathians are the outer rings which emanated from the Imbrium impact. (Days 6-9)

---

[56] Some of the best examples are Theophilus [L12], Aristillus [F10], Copernicus [J7], and Tycho [P8].

[57] The flat floors resulted when molten rocks that were blown upward by the original impact rained back down and spread themselves out more or less smoothly in a thin veneer across the crater floor. Sometimes this material, known as **impact melt**, also landed in the surrounding area outside the crater and can be easily seen today with backyard telescopes. Theophilus [SE/L12] is a good example.

Another major characteristic of basins is that a prodigious amount of debris was blasted out and took flight. When it landed, it left enormous scars in the form of valleys radiating from the impact site. (See Vallis Rheita [Day 4; SE/N14] and the Ptolemaeus region [Day 7; SW/K9].)

Unfortunately, the most splendid example of a multi-ring basin is Mare Orientale, an area that is almost entirely hidden from view except during extreme librations of the southwest limb. During these times you can see the outer ring (the Cordillera Mountains) and maybe even glimpse the inner ring (the Rook Mountains).

crater sequence: (See *Crater Age*)

Dawes Limit: The Dawes Limit is the closest separation of a double star that can be observed for a particular telescope. The formula is $S = 4.56/D$ (S = separation in arc-seconds, D is the diameter of the objective lens or mirror in inches). For example, if your telescope has an 8" mirror, then $S = 4.56/8 = 0.57$ arc-seconds.

"Closest separation" here means that you can barely detect a "figure 8" bulge starting to emerge in the pattern of the two overlapping discs of a double star. A more realistic and esthetically pleasing criterion is the Rayleigh Limit, which occurs when the discs of two stars are separated by a thin black space in between the two stars. The formula for the Rayleigh limit is $S = 5.35/D$ where D is the aperture in inches. So in the above example of an 8-inch telescope, you would expect to see two stars that are separated by 0.67 arc-seconds cleanly split by a thin black space.

dichotomy: The phase of the Moon when half of the disk is illuminated (about Days 7 and 22).

diffraction pattern: (also see *Pickering Seeing Scale*) When you are viewing a star at medium to high power through a refractor with good optics on a night of steady seeing, you will see not a point of light but a central disk, called the Airy disk, surrounded by two or three diffraction rings of light. It is a delicate and beautiful thing to behold, and if the rings are motionless, don't bother to go to bed—you've got an exceptional night! The larger the aperture, the smaller the Airy disk (which is why larger aperture telescopes allow you to see finer detail. It's like looking at a computer image with smaller pixels).

domes: low rounded structures found in mare areas where rising magma has pushed upward and caused the lunar surface to bulge out in blister-like swellings. Sometimes the underlying pressure was not enough to cause the magma to break through, at other times the domes erupted into small, gently sloping shield volcanoes, and their summit pits can actually be seen under low-angle lighting and good seeing conditions.

Lunar domes are not attention grabbers like the more spectacular craters and mountain ranges, so they are easily overlooked—but they are well worth the effort. Because the **endogenic theory** of crater formation has now largely been disproven, it's fun to hunt down evidence that there really was volcanic activity on the Moon. You will need at least six inches of aperture and 150 to 300 power. (Examples: Hortensius Domes [Day 10; NW/J7], Milichius π (pi) [Day 10; NW/H6], Kies π [Day 9; NW/M7], Cauchy ω (omega) and Cauchy τ (tau) [Day 4; NE/J13])

dorsum: (See *wrinkle ridge*)

earthshine: On Day 3 you noticed that the dark side of the Moon was starting to glow softly. This is a phenomenon called *earthshine*. Light from the Sun reflects off the Earth, then bounces to the Moon where it subtly lights up the dark portion beyond the **terminator**. It is a lovely sight, particularly when Venus is close by!

ecliptic: If you were to chart the positions of the planets (including the Sun and the Moon) over several years, you would notice that they never deviate from a fairly narrow path against the background of stars and constellations. This path is called the ecliptic (because it is also the zone where objects will eclipse one another). Why don't we find planets elsewhere in the sky? Because just before the solar system formed there was an enormous cloud of hydrogen gas (mixed with dust particles and chemical elements left over from nearby supernova explosions) which began to collapse in on itself. As the cloud collapsed, it began to spin faster. Centrifugal force caused the cloud to extend itself outward along one plane, while gravity pulled the material in from the cloud's north and south poles. The solid particles and gas, which then coalesced into the Sun and planets, were forced to do so in a fairly narrow plane which today we call the ecliptic.

ejecta blanket: (See *glacis*)

ejection phase: (See *crater formation*)

ejecta patterns: (Also *see splash rays*) You can tell a great deal about the flight path of an incoming projectile by examining the crater it produced and the resulting ejecta patterns. Contrary to what you might expect, craters give no hint of an object's flight path until the angle of the projectile is less than 25°. At this point the crater starts to become elongated, indicating the direction of travel, but the ejected material still remains uniformly circular. At less than 15° this material not only starts to become elongated in the downrange direction, there is a noticeable absence of ejecta in the direction that the impactor came from—what is called the zone of avoidance (also called the forbidden zone).

For very low angles of impact a surprising thing happens: most of the debris does not travel downrange, as we would expect, but splashes out sideways (and somewhat backwards) forming a distinctive butterfly-wing pattern. The ejecta patterns around Proclus [NW/H14] and Tycho [SW/P8] are two of the best examples of what happens during a low angle impact.

endogenic/exogenic theories: Throughout much of the 20th century there was a hotly disputed argument between those who thought that craters were formed by volcanic forces originating from within the Moon (the *endogenic theory*) and those who were convinced that craters were formed when projectiles from elsewhere slammed into the Moon and excavated deep holes (hence *exogenic*). Modern science, thanks to the Apollo missions, has proven that most craters were formed by impact, and even Patrick Moore himself (of *Caldwell Object* fame), the most tenacious supporter of the endogenic theory, had graciously conceded defeat.

fault: a fracture in the lunar surface on either side of which there has been vertical or horizontal movement.

field of view (FOV): The field of view is the diameter of the circle of sky that you can see through the eyepiece of your telescope; the lower the power, the greater the field of view. A simple way to determine the FOV of an eyepiece is to center a small object near the **celestial equator** in the middle of the eyepiece.[58] If your telescope has a motor drive, turn it off, then time how long it takes for the object to drift to the edge. The drift (in seconds) divided by 4 = the field of view in arc-minutes.[59] The Full Moon covers roughly 30 arc-seconds of sky. If you have calculated the FOV of your eyepieces, the following facts will come in handy while you are observing the Moon...

- 1 arc-second at the center of the Moon roughly covers 1 mile (1.15 miles, to be precise).[60]
- 1 mile = 0.87 arc-seconds
- To go from miles to arc-seconds (ballpark figure) subtract about 10 percent, e.g., a100-mi. crater is just short of 90 arc-seconds

---

[58] celestial equator: an imaginary great circle on the celestial sphere that lies directly above the Earth's equator. Any point on the celestial sphere that has a declination zero is on the celestial equator.

[59] For example, if it takes 240 seconds to go from the middle to the edge, then the FOV of your eyepiece = 240/4 = 60' (one degree).

[60] We're assuming the Moon is at mean distance. At apogee and perigee these figures will change slightly. You must also account for the direction and effect of foreshortening as you approach the limb.

floor-fractured crater (FFC): A floor-fractured crater is a special type of crater that has been modified by later volcanism, uplift, and consequent fracturing. Some of the common characteristics of FFC's are that they are large, they have rilles (both arcuate and linear), they occur near the borders of maria, and (most significantly) they are very shallow for their size.

Floor-fractured craters have a fascinating genesis. Some time after the crater was formed and had settled in, magma rising up from underneath the basin actually pushed the crater floors upward (hence their shallowness). It was not an effortless process and the resulting strain caused radial and concentric fractures to appear on the floor. At times, lava would also flow upward through these fractures and spill out onto the crater floor. Examples: *Taruntius* [Day 4; NE/J14], *Petavius* [Days 2-3; SE/M16], *Sabine* [Day 6; NE/J11].

formation of Moon: (See *timeline*)

FOV: (See *field of view*)

ghost crater: When craters formed in low-lying areas, subsequent lava flows at times would just cover them up, but their ghostly outlines remained visible just as breaking ocean waves indicate reefs lying immediately under the surface of the water.

gibbous: More than half but less than fully illuminated.

glacis: The ejecta blanket that surrounds many craters. The traditional meaning of glacis is an artificial slope extending down from a fortification to allow the defenders to have a clear shot at the enemy when they are close. The slope of a lunar glacis will typically be a gentle 5° to 15°.

graben: [German for *ditch*] an elongated depression between two parallel fault lines. These lines occasionally pull apart with such force that the ground between them drops. Rima Ariadaeus [Day 6; NE/J11] and the Alpine Valley [Day 7; NE/E10] are excellent examples of grabens. Lunar grabens have their counterparts on Earth. Examples are Death Valley, parts of the Rhine Valley, and the Rift Valley in Africa.

Hertzsprung-Russel diagram: Plots each star on a graph measuring the star's actual brightness against its temperature and color. By using the diagram, astronomers are able to trace out the life cycle of stars, from young hot proto-stars, through the main sequence phase, to the dying red giant phases.

Highlands: When the Moon was in its molten stage 4.5 bya, lighter aluminum-rich material floated to the surface and created what we know today as the Southern Highlands (a.k.a., Lunar Highlands). The heavier dark basalts sank toward the center of the Moon but later percolated upward through cracks and fissures that were opened up as a result of impacts that created the large basins. This basaltic material filled the "seas" and provides a dark contrast to the much lighter Highlands.

hummocks: low mounds or ridges; small hills

impact melt: When a large asteroid or meteor struck the Moon, so much kinetic energy was released that the immediate surroundings were turned into molten material. This material then flowed freely, sometimes for great distances, covering the lunar terrain with a smooth veneer of impact melt (see Theophilus, [Day 5; SE/L12]).

lacus: lake

late heavy bombardment: (See *Timeline*)

lava tube: At one time there was considerable volcanic activity on the Moon. As the upper parts of a lava flow cooled, a crust formed and the lava continued to flow underneath. When the flow stopped, empty lava tubes were left snaking across the lunar terrain. Later, the roofs of many of these lava tubes caved in, resulting in long sinuous rilles that are visible in amateur telescopes today. Schröter's Valley [Day 11; NW/G5] is the best example of a collapsed lava tube. Today, intact lava tubes are being seriously considered as protective habitats for astronauts and possible colonies.

libration: The apparent back-and-forth wobble of the Moon that can be observed, even by the naked eye, from month to month is called *libration*. The term comes from a Latin word meaning "a rocking movement" around a point of balance.[61] There are three types of libration: in latitude, in longitude, and diurnal. Contrary to popular belief the Moon does not actually rock back and forth. All of these movements are only apparent.

libration in latitude is caused by the fact that the Moon is tilted on its axis by about 6½° to the Earth. This means that as the Moon travels around the Earth, at one point we can see a little over the top of the Moon's north pole, and two weeks later we can see a little underneath the south pole.

libration in longitude is a result of the Moon's orbit being an ellipse. Because the Moon dutifully obeys Kepler's *Three Laws of Planetary Motion*, at **perigee** (its closest point to the Earth) it travels around the Earth more quickly, and at **apogee** (its farthest point) it slows down. However, as it approaches these two points the Moon's speed of rotation on its axis remains constant; only its speed of revolution changes. Think of the Moon as a tennis ball that you've just bounced against the floor in slow motion and that has a slow, steady spin on its axis. At its highest point (apogee) it actually comes to a stop before returning towards the Earth. However, while it's hanging in space, the ball continues to spin slowly on its axis at the same speed, thereby allowing you to peek a little farther around its "edge."

---

[61] Notice the etymological connection with the constellation Libra, "the Scales"—a device which weighs items by using a rocking motion.

diurnal libration happens because as the Earth spins on its axis, you (the observer standing on the Earth's surface) are actually carried through space several thousand miles between the times of moonrise and moonset. This means that at moonrise you are able to see a little bit around the right "edge" of the Moon, and at moonset the Earth has carried you to a new vantage point up to 8,000 miles away from where you started. You can now see around its other edge, thus allowing the Moon to appear as if it had just wobbled its face a bit left and right. The amount of libration in longitude can be up to three degrees.

For an excellent visual demonstration of the effects of libration, go to the following website:

http://en.wikipedia.org/wiki/File:Lunar_libration_with_phase_Oct_2007.gif

Then click on the image of the Moon to start the demonstration.

limb: the rim of the visible disk of the Moon

locked rotation: (also called *synchronous rotation*) Everybody knows that the Moon keeps the same face pointed toward the Earth. Few people know why. It has to do with one simple law and one easily understandable fact. *The Law:* (If you have a natural aversion to formulas, just bear with me to the next sentence.) The pull of gravity on objects is in inverse proportion to the square of the distance between them. Simply put: if an object is moved twice as far away, it will feel only ¼ of the original gravitational pull (i.e., four is the square of two; one-fourth is the "inverse proportion" of four).[62] This means that if you move an object just a *little bit closer*, the increase in gravitational pull is markedly greater, which brings us to...

The Fact: Shortly after the Moon was created 4.6 bya, it remained molten throughout for a very long time and, unlike today, spun rapidly and completely

---

[62] We have Sir Isaac Newton to thank for this law.

on its axis. As it spun, huge tidal waves of molten material were raised on its surface due to the gravitational pull of the Earth. As the surface of the Moon cooled, this tidal bulge was eventually locked into place and the Moon was permanently deformed from a circle into an ellipse.[63] Because the Earth exhibits a greater gravitational pull on the long axis of this ellipse than on the rest of the Moon, the Earth's gravity locked onto the bulge and held it firmly in place. The near side of the Moon has been wincing ever since, but cannot escape our grip!

LPD: Lunar Pyroclastic Deposit (See *pyroclastic*)

LTP: (See *lunar transient phenomenon*)

lunar day: This *Guide* is built around the *Lunar Day* number, meaning the number of days since the last New Moon (called the *synodic month*). There are about 29 days in the lunar cycle. Once you have determined what Lunar Day you wish to observe on,[64] then simply turn to that day in the *Guide* to get a list of the most interesting features that are observable for the night in question. Keep in mind that the current **libration** may be so extreme that you might have to go forward or backward one day to find objects that are ideally close to the **terminator**. (See *selenographic colongitude*.)

lunar month: There are several different ways to define a lunar month. For our purposes, the most important of these is the *synodic month*, the period from New Moon to New Moon (also called a *lunation*). The average synodic month is 29d 12h 44m.[65] Keep in mind that **New Moon** can occur at any clock hour during the day or night, and on the following month it will occur at a different time.

---

[63] Technically, into an oblate spheroid.

[64] Astronomy apps such as *SkySafari Plus, Deluxe Moon Standard, Lunatic* will give you the current lunar day.

[65] However, this can vary by up to 12 hours because the orbit of the Moon, as well as the Earth, is an ellipse. As a result, the Moon's orbital speed will increase when it is close to the Earth and decrease when it is farther away.

lunar transient phenomenon (LTP): A lunar transient phenomenon is a short-lived change in the appearance of the lunar surface. LTP's are usually variations in lighting (either sudden or gradual) or color. They often manifest themselves as obscurations, foggy patches, etc. Enough LTP reports have been made by reputable individuals that scientists have reluctantly conceded that such things do occur. Of the reputable sightings that have been made, fully one-third has occurred around the Aristarchus Plateau [NW/G5]. So keep your eyes on this region. You might get lucky!

lunation: The period of time taken for the Moon to go through a complete cycle of phases (see *lunar month*).

mare: (*pl. maria*) Latin for *sea*. The large dark areas that cover nearly a third of the near side of the Moon were once thought to be actual seas and were therefore called *maria* (a termed that was coined by Galileo himself).[66] We tend to think of craters as comparatively small objects and lose sight of the fact that large lunar "seas" are the result of impacts also. Basically, if it's round it's a crater.

The light and dark areas of the Moon indicate that it is made up of at least two different materials: When the Moon was molten 4.5 bya, lighter aluminum-rich material floated to the surface (this material was lighter both in terms of its color and its density) and heavier, darker material sank toward the center. When the large basins were created, they filled up with the darker interior basalts that flowed to the surface through the many cracks and fissures that opened up, forming the many dark seas that are clearly visible to the naked eye today.

mascons: Areas of the Moon's surface that were discovered to have unusually strong local gravitational effects due to concentrations of dense, thick lunar

---

[66] Some sources say it was Kepler.

material [formed from *mas(s)* + *con(centration)*]. Mascons are prevalent around lunar swirls (see Reiner Gamma [Day 12; NW/J4]).

Meteor Crater: An impact crater in Arizona that is .75 miles wide and 250 feet deep. It was formed 50,000 years ago when a meteorite, about 160 feet in diameter, slammed into the desert at about 10 miles per second. The energy released was the equivalent of about 20 megatons of TNT—about 1,300 times more powerful than the Hiroshima bomb!

modification phase: (See *crater formation*)

Moon facts...
> Age: 4.5 billion years[67]
> Diameter: 2,160 mi.
> Av. distance: 238,856 mi.
>> at perigee: 221,457 mi.
>> at apogee: 252,712 mi.
> Av. angular diameter: 31' 05"[68]
>> at perigee: 33' 28.8"
>> at apogee: 29' 23.2"
> Magnitude at Full Moon: -12.55
> Av. angular velocity of Moon through sky: 33 arc-minutes per hour.
>> (The Moon will travel its own diameter in two minutes.)
> Av. orbital velocity around Earth: 2,287 mph
>> Sidereal orbital period:[69] 27d 7h 43m 11.5s
>> Recession speed: about 1.5 inches per year[70]

---

[67] Making it only 30-50 million years younger than the Earth.

[68] This is half the width of your index fingernail held at arm's length.

[69] *Sidereal:* with respect to the stars. Because the Earth has circled farther around the Sun during a month, the Moon must now travel farther to come back to its starting point in relation to the Sun and have the same appearance.

[70] i.e., the Moon is receding from the Earth at 1.5 inches/year

Moore, Patrick: Sir Patrick Caldwell-Moore (1923-2012), a British astronomer who was well known for his many books, articles, and radio and TV programs on astronomy. He particularly specialized on the Moon and created the Caldwell Catalogue, a list of 109 of his own favorite astronomical objects that was designed to complement the Messier Catalogue. (See *Messier* in *Glossary*.)

morphology: (See *crater morphology*)

multi-ring basins: (See *crater morphology: basins*)

New Moon: A New Moon occurs when the Moon is between the Earth and the Sun. Technically speaking, a New Moon is invisible because it is so close to the Sun that only the dark side of the Moon faces the Earth, but the first observable crescent is commonly referred to as a New Moon.

nimbus: The dark, circular melt-deposits which appear around the outside rims of some young craters. After a billion years or so of constant micrometeorite bombardment these features (along with their cousins, the lunar rays) disappear. The Moon's best example of both nimbus and rays is Tycho [SW/P8].

perigee: the point at which the Moon is closest to the Earth in its elliptical orbit.

photometry: the science of measuring the intensity and other characteristics of light.

Pickering Seeing Scale: (Also see *Antoniadi Seeing Scale*) This is a scale by which you can quantify the seeing conditions, particularly as you are observing double stars, but it is useful for the Moon also. It ranks the quality of seeing from 1 to 10—the higher the number the better the seeing. This scale was devised by

William H. Pickering using a 5" refractor; results may vary for your own instrument. Diffraction rings, which are an important part of the Pickering Seeing Scale, [71] are rarely observable on reflectors because of interference from the central obstruction (the secondary mirror). However, if your reflector is large enough you can duplicate the quality of a refractor by placing a mask over the front opening. [72] The mask will allow you to see clearly defined diffraction rings and Airy disks when the seeing permits.

The Pickering ratings are as follows:[73]

1) Very bad: Star image is usually about twice the diameter of the third diffraction ring (if the ring could be seen)—approximately 13 arc-seconds in diameter.

2) Very bad: Image occasionally twice the diameter of the third ring.

3) Very bad: Image about the same diameter as the third ring (about 7 arc-seconds) and brighter at the center.

4) Poor: Central Airy disk often visible. Arcs of diffraction rings sometimes seen on brighter stars.

5) Poor: Airy disk always visible. Arcs frequently seen on brighter stars.

6) Good: Airy disk always visible; short arcs constantly seen.

7) Good: Airy disk sometimes sharply defined. Diffraction rings seen as long arcs or complete circles.

---

[71] When you are viewing a star at medium to high power through a refractor with good optics on a night of reasonably good seeing, you will not see a point of light but a central disk, called the Airy disk, surrounded by two or three *diffraction rings* of light. The larger the telescope, the smaller the Airy disk.

[72] Cut a circular piece of posterboard the size of the outside diameter of your telescope tube. Then with a compass and an X-Acto knife cut a hole which will just cover the distance between the edge of the secondary mirror and the edge of the primary mirror. Tape this mask over the end of the telescope tube (being careful to place the hole between the secondary supports). Although this will reduce the aperture of your scope, it will remove the central obstruction and give you sharp images with full, undiminished contrast.

[73] For an animated visual on what each of the ratings means, go to http://www.damianpeach.com/pickering.htm.

8) Excellent: Disk always sharply defined. Rings seen as long arcs or complete circles, but always in motion.

9) Excellent: Inner diffraction ring is stationary. Outer rings momentarily stationary.

10) Perfect: no motion. Diffraction-limited seeing.[74]

precession of the equinoxes: The Earth has a wobbling motion as it spins on its axis, much like a top. This is caused by the gravitational attraction of the Moon and the Sun on the Earth's equatorial bulge. As a result, the point where the **celestial equator** crosses the ecliptic (called the *equinox*—a time when the lengths of night and day are equal) slowly moves westward by 1° every 72 years. This means, for example, that on the first day of spring (defined as the moment that the Sun crosses the celestial equator on its way north) the Sun will be found in a different constellation every couple of thousand years. This is why astrology has slowly gotten out of sync with real science. If your astrological sign is, for example, Aquarius, the Sun was actually *not* in Aquarius when you were born (as it would have been 2,000 years ago) but in Capricornus, the next constellation going west. Modern astrologers will say that they have known about precession for a very long time, as, indeed, they have. Ptolemy was completely aware of precession, but astrology has been around since the second millennium BCE and at some point astrologers were blindsided by precession and were obliged to redefine the meaning of astrological "houses," saying they had nothing to do with the background constellations.

pyroclastic eruptions: A substance that is composed chiefly of rock fragments of volcanic origin is called pyroclastic (from two Greek words meaning *broken by fire*). On the Moon it refers to a little known but fascinating phenomenon

---

[74] i.e., the image is perfect for the size of telescope you are using and cannot be improved upon.

called explosive pyroclastic eruptions. As magma and molten rocks spewed out from volcanic vents, sometimes gases that were trapped within suddenly expanded and caused the rocks to explode in a shower of tiny dark glass beads. The result was that the area surrounding the source vent was covered by a dark halo of pyroclastic deposits. There are several areas on the Moon where you can see these deposits through backyard telescopes, but the crater Alphonsus [Day 7; SW/L9] is the best example. The Aristarchus Plateau [Day 11; NW/G4-5] is entirely covered with pyroclastic ash 30-100 feet thick. The Plateau has attracted the attention of NASA as an area for lunar colonization because hydrogen and oxygen can be extracted from the ash, providing fuel, water, and breathable air.

resolution: the smallest separation between two objects which allows them just to be distinguished as separate. This will vary depending on the quality of the optics, atmospheric turbulence, one's experience and age, etc. A dependable formula for distinguishing the smallest recognizable crater (as opposed to a dot) is 9/D, where D is the aperture of the telescope in inches (e.g., a 10" telescope could resolve a crater 0.9 miles in diameter). Keep in mind that rilles (because they are lines, not dots) can be discerned when they have even smaller widths. To help you in determining how small a crater you can observe with your particular telescope, the back of the Field Map lists all the craters with their diameters.

To calculate your personal naked eye resolution, draw two dark lines separated by a 1mm space on a piece of paper. Attach the paper to a wall and slowly back away until you can no longer distinguish a separation between the two lines, then move forward until you can barely see the separation and measure the distance from your eyes to the paper in millimeters. (In the following formula, θ [theta] is the angle in arc-minutes that your naked eyes can resolve; D is the distance in millimeters from your eyes to the lines on the wall.)

$$\theta = (1mm/D) \times (3437.75)\,[75]$$

---

[75] I am indebted to Mike Siddoway, professor of mathematics at Colorado College, for working out this formula for personal eye resolution.

rilles: The word *rille* comes from a German word meaning *groove* (Latin form: *rima*) and describes any of various long narrow depressions that resemble a channel or valley. There are three types of rilles found on the Moon: sinuous, arcuate, and linear. The best place to see rilles is just west of the Sea of Tranquillity around Days 6 and 7. In the areas between Mare Vaporum and Sinus Medii you will find a remarkably varied collection—to wit, Rima Ariadaeus, Rima Hyginus, and the Triesnecker complex [J10-11]. Also the eastern shore of Mare Humorum [M6-7] has an abundance of rilles.

> **arcuate rilles:** (Also see *Floor-Fractured Craters*) As the maria filled up with heavy basalts they would sink under the increased weight, opening up arcuate (i.e., curved) cracks around the basin perimeters. Often two or more parallel arcuate rilles would form. A noteworthy example is the Hippalus rilles [Day 10; SW/M6-7] on the eastern shore of Mare Humorum.

> **sinuous rilles:**[76] These are volcanic in origin and are thought to be collapsed lava tubes that carried lava from their source down to the plains below. In some instances it is possible to see the originating volcano at one end of these rilles. As the upper layers of a lava flow cooled, a substantial crust was formed and the lava continued to flow underneath. When the flow stopped, empty lava tubes were left snaking across the lunar terrain. Later, the roofs of many of these lava tubes collapsed, resulting in long sinuous rilles that are visible in amateur telescopes today. Schröter's Valley [Day 11; NW/G5] is the best example of a sinuous rille with its originating volcano, the Cobra Head.

> **linear rilles:** These are thought to be **grabens**, sections of the lunar terrain that had sunk between two parallel fault lines. Rima Hyginus [Day 6; J10]

---

[76] *sinuous:* having many curves

is an excellent example. (Technically, the Alpine Valley [Day 7; NE/E10] is a graben, but it's so large that it's just called a valley.)

rima: (pl. *rimae*; see *rille*)

ring features: (See *crater morphology: basins*)

rupes: (See *scarp*)

scarp (Latin: *rupes*): a long cliff or steep slope that results from faulting or is part of a multi-ring fragment that resulted from a major impact that created one of the basins. The two best examples are Rupes Recta (the Straight Wall) [Day 8; NW/M9] and the Altai Scarp [Day 5; SE/M12].

SCL: (See *selenographic colongitude*)

sculpting: Valleys on the Earth were created primarily by two processes: movement of the Earth's crust (plate tectonics) and erosion. These processes do not exist on the Moon, but there *is* an abundance of valleys. Sculpting is the most important process that contributed to their formation. When a major impact occurred (the kind that blasted out the large basins) mountain-sized boulders took flight, often in linear formations, and when they landed they dug out long radial valleys that today point directly back, with accusing fingers, to their explosive place of origin. Pay particular attention to the area around Ptolemaeus [Day 7; SW/K9]. This is lunar sculpting at its best, and many valleys on the Moon owe their existence to this process. Examples: Rheita Valley [Day 4; SE/N14], Hipparchus [Day 7; SE/K10], and the Ptolemaeus-Albategnius region [Day 7; SW/K9].

secondary craters: When many of the larger craters like Copernicus were formed, the impact ejected thousands of fragments, some of them quite large. When these fragments landed, they formed smaller craters of their own, which can be seen today surrounding the parent crater.

selenographic colongitude (SCL): Selenography is the study of the physical features of the Moon (from *selene*, the Greek word for moon).

The SCL is the position of the sunrise terminator as measured in degrees westward from the prime meridian, the zero longitude line running down the middle of the Moon. It is usually referred to, more simply, as the *colongitude*. (See *terminator* below)

shadow hiding: Contrary to what logic would lead us to believe, the Full Moon is not twice as bright as a half Moon, it is actually 10 times brighter! This is due to an effect called *shadow hiding*. When we see the Moon at first quarter, the sun casts long shadows near the terminator (it is, after all, late evening on the Moon). These shadows extend not only from large mountain peaks, but also from every small pebble and rock on the surface of the Moon. The cumulative effect diminishes the overall brightness of a half Moon by a factor of 10 compared to a Full Moon. (Think of yourself as living in Kansas. At the moment of sunset, your shadow will literally stretch to the horizon!)

simple crater: (See *crater morphology*)

sinus: bay

solar wind: A continuous outflow from the Sun of electrons, protons, and the nuclei of elements such as helium. At the distance of the Earth, these particles travel at around 500 miles per second. The solar wind, along with micrometeorite bombardment, actually contributes to erosion on the Moon and eventually wipes out splash rays and the dark collars surrounding some craters like Tycho.

Although the effects of the solar wind over a short period of time are miniscule, the cumulative effect is impressive. If you take a 1,000 square meter Mylar sail and put it on a surfboard in outer space, the solar wind will slowly push against it. After six weeks you will be surfing along at 24,000 miles per hour!

splash rays: (Also see *ejecta pattern*) Splash rays are typically made up of brighter material that had been excavated from below the dark mare basalts during major impacts and then blown across the lunar surface for up to a thousand miles. All craters were originally surrounded by splash rays, but these rays disappeared after a billion years or so of micrometeorite bombardment and weathering by the solar wind. Rays become increasingly prominent as the Moon approaches full. It is often assumed that the texture of lunar rays resembles light, fluffy face powder, but rays are also composed of crushed rock and boulders that are up to a couple of feet in diameter. Large rays are commonly several feet thick and would be difficult for an astronaut to walk through.

subsidence: After the large basins formed, heavy lava rose up through the cracks and fissures that were opened up. The additional weight caused many of the basins to sink toward the center. As a result, shoreline craters would tilt, and sometimes their seaward rims would actually sink below "sea level." It used to be thought that the inward facing rims of these craters simply melted away because of the intense heat generated by the mare lavas. That explanation has now fallen into disrepute. Charles Wood points out that if that were the case, the rims of these breached craters would not systematically decrease in height toward the basin center, as they do in a large number of instances. Examples are Daguerre and Fracastorius on the shores of Mare Nectaris, Posidonius in eastern Serenitatis (all on Day 5), and Sinus Iridum, the magnificent bay on the northwest shore of Imbrium (Day 10).

subtend: to fix or mark the limits of, to span. At 100 yards, an angle of 1 arc-second would span the width of a pinhead. At the mean distance of the Moon, it would widen out to enclose only 1 mile.

SuperMoon: Because the orbit of the Moon around the Earth is elliptical,[77] a few times a year the Full Moon will coincide with its closest **perigee**.[78] As a result, it will appear 14% larger and 30% brighter. This is an event worth planning for (check Google for the current "SuperMoon"). Take out a lawn chair, some music, and a bottle of wine. Find a clear view of the eastern horizon and be in place *while* the Moon is rising, rather than later when it might be technically closer to the earth but will appear smaller. When the Moon just clears the horizon, the standard illusion that the Moon is bigger will be combined with the fact that it really *is* bigger—a double whammy that is a captivating sight!

An *extreme* SuperMoon is something that happens comparatively rarely, and for a few days preceding such an event the terminally gullible will be coming out of the woodwork predicting earthquakes, volcanoes, hurricanes, plagues, and kindred harbingers of Armageddon. So get your front row seat and don't miss the excitement!

A similar mindset was running amuck during the appearance of the supernova of 1572 when the famous German painter George Bush (no relation) said that the apparition "will cause all sorts of mischief such as pestilence, sudden death, bad weather, and Frenchmen." (I'll leave it to the reader to sort out the relative seriousness of these calamities.)

swirls: Lunar swirls are one of the more curious features on the Moon and they have baffled scientists for a long time. No known geological process could have created them, and to heighten the mystery, instruments on the Apollo spacecraft measured strong magnetic fields directly over the swirls.

---

[77] Kepler's discovery of the three laws of planetary motion was a major step toward freeing us from the shackles imposed for centuries by Aristotle, Ptolemy, and the Roman Catholic Church—all of whom insisted that planets must move in perfect circles.

[78] The Moon will come to perigee once a month, but the perigee distance can vary by up to 8,700 miles, so having a Full Moon coincide with its closest perigee is something that's worth paying a little attention to (it will happen up to six times per year). The term "SuperMoon" was actually coined by the astrologer Richard Nolle in 1979 to describe either a Full Moon or a New Moon which coincides with perigee. However, the astronomical community insists on the official term "perigee-syzygy" (probably out of an understandable reluctance to admit that astrologers might have a point)—but "SuperMoon" is so much easier to say!

It was discovered that tiny particles connected with these swirls become statically charged, particularly around local sunset and sunrise, and hover just above the lunar surface. Up to now, no one has discovered why this happens. Reiner Gamma is the best-known example of a lunar swirl [Day 12; NW/J4].

T-numbers: Immediately following each Day entry you will find a "T-number" which indicates the longitude of the terminator, the dividing line between the sunlit and dark portions of the Moon. Features on the Moon look quite dramatic when they are within 10° or so of the terminator. However the T-number assumes that the Moon has no **libration** (the apparent rocking back and forth of the Moon) so the actual longitude of the terminator on the night you are observing may vary up to 7° from the T-number that is listed.

terminator: The line dividing the light and dark portions of the Moon. If you were standing on the terminator you would experience lunar sunset or sunrise. When you are observing the Moon through a telescope, the areas close to the terminator are the most exciting places to view because the long shadows turn the landscape into an unforgettable wonderland! As the Moon rotates on its axis, the terminator creeps across the Moon at approximately 10 miles per hour (which corresponds roughly to 9 arc-seconds at the mean distance of the Moon).[79] Because of the combined effects of this movement with libration, features listed for a particular lunar day in this *Guide* might not be ideally placed for viewing vis-à-vis the terminator. Accordingly, you might wish to go forward or backward by one day.

Although the *Lunar Day* works well enough for most purposes, the current longitude of the terminator is more helpful for figuring out the visibility of specific features. Some of these features (like the "Lunar-X" and various domes)

---

[79] A circle is divided into 360°—a degree has 60 arc-minutes, and one arc-minute is divided into 60 arc-seconds. (This is pretty small stuff—a pinhead at 100 yards covers one arc-second.) A low-power eyepiece will typically show more than 30 arc-minutes (the width of the Full Moon).

have a very narrow viewing window, and there are times when you might prefer to use it. As of this writing, *Moon Map Pro* is the only app which gives you the longitude of the terminator. You can download it from iTunes.

terraces: Stair-stepped terrain found around the inside slopes of large impact craters, caused by the slumping of large sections of the interior of crater walls. Terraces are a major feature of Tycho-class craters.

TIMELINE:

4.5 bya:[80] It is not often that the term "earth shaking" can be used without hyperbole, but radioactive dating tells us that 60 million years after the formation of the Earth a Mars-sized object slammed into the Earth and shook our planet so severely that it nearly disintegrated (an event that is often referred to as "the Big Whack.") Enormous amounts of debris were sent into orbit around the Earth, and in a surprisingly short amount of time the Moon coalesced out of this material.[81]

While the Moon was still in a plastic state, heavier materials sank toward the center, and lighter materials (both in weight and in color) floated to the surface. As a result, the Lunar Highlands remain bright while the "seas," which are covered by lava that oozed up from the lower regions, are dark. At one time, before the seas flowed, the entire surface of the Moon was as bright as the Highlands.

At the time of its creation the Moon orbited only 14,000 miles away from the Earth (instead of the current 240,000 miles). It would have appeared 17 times larger in the sky and orbited the Earth in just a few hours! The Moon is currently receding from the Earth by about 1½ inches per year, but as it recedes its period of rotation also slows, so it will always keep the same face towards the Earth.

---

[80] bya: billion years ago

[81] Logic tells us that it would require millions of years for such a process to take place. Scientists working from computer models say that it was only a matter of months!

However, because of this recession, our descendants will eventually be deprived of ever seeing a total solar eclipse because the Moon will be too small to cover the Sun completely.

We owe a huge debt of gratitude to the Moon. Its presence is a major factor in the formation of life on Earth. The Moon stabilizes the tilt of the Earth's axis at a lifesaving 23.5° in relation to the ecliptic (the narrow path along which the Sun and the planets appear to move). It is this tilt which gives us our mild seasons. During the summer in the northern hemisphere the axis of the Earth is inclined towards the Sun; therefore, we receive more heat. Six months later the Earth is on the opposite side of the Sun and its axis is tilted away, so the northern hemisphere receives less energy and it is winter. The opposite is true for the southern hemisphere.[82] Without the Moon's overriding influence, the gravitational torques imposed by the Sun, Jupiter, and Saturn would cause the angle of the Earth's axis to fluctuate so dramatically (possibly by up to 90°) that higher forms of life could never have developed due to the deadly swing of inhospitable seasons.

4.5-3.9 bya: *Pre-Nectarian period.* characterized by intense meteorite and asteroid bombardment. The lunar crust formed during this time.

4.1-3.8 bya: *Late Heavy Bombardment.* This is a period of explosive activity when most of the craters on the Moon formed. In spite of appearances, asteroids and comets did not single out the Moon for special treatment during this period. The Earth received the same number of impacts per square mile, but the eroding effects of wind, rain, and tectonic activity (which are not present on the Moon) obliterated most of the evidence here on Earth.

3.92-3.85 bya: *Nectarian period.* This period begins with the formation of the Nectaris Basin and ends with the impact that created the Mare Imbrium basin.

---

[82] In a survey of Harvard students and their professors some years ago, 50% of them could not explain why it's hot in the summer—most of them believing it was because the Earth was closer to the Sun (it's actually farther away)!

The densely cratered terrain found in the Lunar Highlands was formed by ejecta from Nectaris. The oldest lunar features formed prior to this event.

3.85 bya: The Imbrium basin forms when an asteroid 60 miles in diameter slams into the Moon at 10 miles per second and blasts out a 720-mile-wide crater! This event closes out the Nectarian period.

3.2-1.1 bya: *the Eratosthenian age.* This was the longest period in lunar history during which lava still flowed as a result of late-stage volcanism and continued to fill low-lying areas, particularly around Mare Imbrium and Oceanus Procellarum. Many pre-existing craters during this period of heavy lava flow were partially or completely covered, leaving tantalizing images of their subsurface existence. Many of these "ghost craters" are visible today with backyard telescopes.

1.0 bya to present: The Copernican period when the "youngest" and freshest craters were formed. Most of these craters can be identified by the bright ray systems surrounding them. (These *splash rays* disappear after a billion years or so of micrometeorite bombardment.)

Tycho-class craters: These are splendid craters with complex central mountain peaks, flat floors, ejecta blankets, and palatial stair-step terraces resulting from enormous landslides.

valley (Latin: *vallis*): Unlike valleys on the Earth that were created slowly by the effects of water erosion, plate tectonics, and the inexorable creep of glaciers, the appearance of most of the valleys on the Moon was sudden and spectacular. They were the result of material that was ejected during the formation of the major basins when mountain-sized objects were violently blasted from the impact zones. Sometimes these objects took flight in precisely aligned groups which, when they crashed back onto the lunar surface, created long scars that today point back to their place of origin. If you look closely at these features (such as Vallis Rheita [Day 3; SE/N14]) you might be able to detect that they are not continuous unbroken valleys but are made up of a series of individual overlapping craters. Some other valleys are ***grabens***, parallel fault lines that have pulled apart, allowing the terrain in between to sink. The Moon's best example of a graben is the Alpine Valley (*Vallis Alpes*) [Day 7; NE/E10].

Virtual Moon Atlas: Two Frenchmen, Christian LeGrand and Patrick Chevalley, have created a software program called *Virtual Moon Atlas* that is the finest lunar program available. Incredibly, they offer it at no charge and it is available for Mac, Windows and Linux platforms (but not mobile devices). You can download it for free from *http://ap-i.net/avl/en/download* (or Google "Virtual Moon Atlas"). Then click on "How to Support Us" and make a donation to thank Christian and Patrick for their gift to the astronomy world.

waxing/waning: Beginners are sometimes confused about whether the Moon is waxing (growing larger) or waning. Here's a helpful tip: Curve your fingers and thumb around the round part of the Moon (you will naturally use the right or left hand, depending on which way the Moon is facing), then place the flat of your other hand against the open fingers to form either a "b" (*before* Full Moon) or a lower case "a" (*after* Full Moon).

wrinkle ridges: Low ridge-like features on the maria which can be seen only at lunar sunrise or sunset. Although the official term is *dorsa*, they are more popularly known as *wrinkle ridges*. The most prominent and beautiful example on the Moon is the *Serpentine Ridge* in the Sea of Serenity [Day 5; NE/G12], known officially by the decidedly less poetic name of *Dorsa Smirnov*.

Wood, Charles: Charles Wood is a lunar scientist with a PhD in Planetary Geology from Brown University. He writes a monthly article on the Moon for *Sky & Telescope*, worked for NASA in several capacities, created the Lunar Photo of the Day website, and wrote the highly acclaimed book *The Modern Moon: A Personal View* (Sky Publishing Corp., Cambridge, Massachusetts 2003).

Appendix A: Historical Notes

Many of the features on the Moon are named after famous historical figures (scholars, scientists, artists, and explorers). Since it would be helpful to have at least a speaking acquaintance with these individuals, as you encounter their namesake craters in the main text of this *Guide* you are referred to this section by the symbol †.

Archimedes: (287 BCE-212 BCE) Greek mathematician, inventor, and astronomer who most famously was given the problem of determining whether the king's crown was truly made out of solid gold, but he was charged not to damage the crown in any way. He worked on the problem for quite awhile, then as he was taking a bath one evening, he noticed that when he submerged his leg in the water, the water rose. He instantly realized that submerging the crown in water would displace an amount of water exactly equal to the volume of the crown, thus he could compare the volume to the density of gold. According to the story, he was so excited that he jumped out of the tub and ran naked down the street shouting, "Eureka, I have found it!" As it turned out, the goldsmith who had made the crown had duped the king and made off with some of the gold.

Aristarchus of Samos: (310-230 BCE) Greek astronomer who was the first person to teach that the Earth orbited around the Sun and rotated on its axis, hence he is frequently referred to as the "Greek Copernicus." (Tragically, most of his writings went up in flames when the Great Library at Alexandria was burned.) For his belief that the Sun was at the center of the Solar System, it was suggested by Cleanthes the Stoic that he should be punished for impertinence to the gods. (It took awhile, but the idea eventually caught on. Eighteen hundred years later, the monk Giordano Bruno [83] was burned at the stake in Rome for making similar suggestions.)

Aristotle: (384-322 BCE) Greek philosopher, student of Plato, and teacher of Alexander the Great. Because Aristotle believed that the circle was the "perfect" shape, he taught that the universe was spherical, finite, and centered on the Earth. But he also was one of the first scholars to teach that the Earth was round. This was not based on a fanciful belief in the "perfection" of spheres, but on scientific evidence: He simply noticed that as one travelled north, the otherwise immovable North Star rose higher over the horizon. The only possible explanation was that the Earth was round. He also knew that lunar eclipses were caused by the shadow of the Earth, which was unmistakably curved.

Brahe, Tycho: (1546-1601) Brilliant (albeit eccentric) Danish astronomer who had a passion for understanding how the stars and planets moved. He tirelessly recorded their positions with great precision and without the benefit of a telescope. (It is said that he could resolve an angular separation as small as 6/10 of an arc-minute with his naked eyes. A normal person with good eyesight can resolve between 1 and 4 arc-minutes.)

In November of 1572, Brahe extensively reported on the discovery (not his own) of a bright new star—what today we call a supernova. "Tycho's Star," as it came to be known, caused quite a stir because its sudden appearance meant that the heavens were not immutable and perfect after all—such was the belief introduced by Aristotle and insisted on by the Catholic Church. But because the prevailing religion in Denmark was Lutheranism, Brahe suffered no repercussions.

Arguably, next to his meticulous calculations, the greatest thing Brahe did was to bequeath his logbooks to Johaness Kepler, his assistant. After studying Brahe's fastidious entries on the positions of Mars, Kepler made the crucial

---

[83] Bruno's crimes included a diverse list of other so-called heresies, such as asserting the existence of other inhabited worlds and not believing in the Trinity, the divinity of Christ, or the virgin birth.

discovery that planets moved in ellipses, not perfect circles. From that point on the movement of the planets became much more predictable.

Caesar, Julius:[84] (100 BCE-44 BCE) Roman general and statesman who, because of his conquests, amassed an enormous amount of power. When he was ordered by the Senate to stand trial for various charges, he marched on Rome with his armies and emerged as the undisputed leader of the Roman world. Contrary to popular opinion, Julius Caesar was not the emperor of Rome but the "Dictator in Perpetuity" who transformed Rome from a Republic to an Empire. It was his heir, Augustus, who was the first emperor. Julius was assassinated on March 14, 44 BCE, by a group of senators who wished to restore the constitutional Republic.

Cassini, Giovanni-Domenico: (1625-1712) Italian-born astronomer who moved to France in 1669 and became director of the Paris Observatory in 1671. He discovered four of Saturn's moons and the so-called Cassini Division within Saturn's rings. He co-discovered the Great Red Spot on Jupiter and was the first to observe Jupiter's differential rotation. In spite of his many talents, Cassini refused to accept the findings of his young assistant, Olaus Roemer, that light had a finite speed, believing that it was propagated instantaneously. By clocking the orbital period of Jupiter's moon Io, Roemer measured the speed of light to be 140,000 miles per second (reasonably close to today's figure). Cassini never admitted he was wrong, even when presented with irrefutable evidence.

Copernicus, Nicolaus: (1473-1543) Renowned Polish astronomer who took the first major step to bringing astronomy out of the dark ages. The convoluted system of cycles and epicycles that Ptolemy introduced to explain the movement of the planets was woefully inadequate. Calculations of planetary positions were

---

[84] In Shakespeare's play by the same name, Caesar's wife, Calpurnia, begs her husband not to go out on the Ides of March. A comet was observed the night before, and she says prophetically, "When beggars die, there are no comets seen. The heavens themselves blaze forth the death of princes."

always off. Copernicus realized that if he simply placed the Sun at the center of the solar system, suddenly the math worked! Astronomers could predict the positions of the planets with greater accuracy (although because he still insisted that planets must move in "perfect circles," calculations were still a little off. It was Kepler who put things straight some 60 years later with his discovery of elliptical orbits.)

Copernicus published his findings in his book, *De Revolutionibus Orbium Coelestium* (*On the Revolutions of the Heavenly Spheres*). The book was essentially finished by 1532, but because he feared ridicule from the academic world and reprisals from the Catholic Church, he did not allow it to be published until he was on his deathbed in 1543. He was presented with a copy of the book on the very day that he died.

Eratosthenes: (275-195 BCE) Greek astronomer, mathematician, and chief librarian of the Great Library in Alexandria, a repository of knowledge that had not been rivaled until the creation of the Library of Congress!

At one point Eratosthenes ingeniously calculated the circumference of the Earth using deductive reasoning that is within the grasp of any clever high school student today. At the summer solstice in Alexandria, the Sun, at its highest point, cast a shadow that had an angle of 7° 12'. Eratosthenes had heard that at noon on the same day in Syene, a city that was due south of Alexandria, the Sun shown directly down a deep well without casting a shadow. He realized that these two facts placed him on the verge of a monumental discovery. He hired a man to pace off the distance between Alexandria and Syene, which came to be 5,000 stadia (about 500 miles). Since 7° 12' is one-fiftieth of a circle, Eratosthenes calculated the circumference of the Earth to be 25,000 miles. He was only 100 miles off!

Eratosthenes' greatest accomplishment was the library at Alexandria, which, at its peak, contained nearly one million books in the form of papyrus scrolls. He had a rather clever way of making sure he had the largest collection of books in the world: Whenever a ship came into port, Eratosthenes arranged with the King to have it detained until his army of scribes copied all the books that were on board! The books were then returned. The library was tragically burnt to the ground and Western civilization lost one of its greatest treasures.

There are several theories about who was responsible for the fire. Some say it was Julius Caesar who, on a campaign to Greece in 47 BCE, set fire to Greek ships in the harbor. The fire then inadvertently spread to the city and the library was destroyed. Another theory was that Theophilus, the Bishop of Alexandria, had become intolerant of the pagans' growing influence and ordered a mob to destroy the Serapis temple (which also served as a sister library to the main one in Alexandria and contained 42,000 scrolls).

One of the more interesting theories is that Muslim armies attacked the city in 645 CE and Caliph Omar, when he heard that the library contained "all the knowledge of the world," is reputed to have said of its holdings, "They will either contradict the Koran, in which case they are heresy, or they will agree with it, so they are superfluous." As a result he ordered the library destroyed.

Eudoxus: (410-350 BCE) Greek astronomer and student of Plato who created a system of 27 spheres to account for the movement of the celestial bodies. This model of the solar system, in various forms and modifications (most famously by Ptolemy), persisted until Copernicus in the 1500s.

Galilaei, Galileo: (1564-1642) Italian scientist, philosopher, mathematician and astronomer who was dubbed "the Father of Modern Science" by Albert Einstein because he was the first person who actually conducted experiments to prove his theories!

Galileo first pointed his telescope towards the heavens in 1609 and revolutionized astronomy with his discoveries that Jupiter had moons (proving that the Earth was not the center of all movement), that Venus went through phases (proving that it orbited the Sun, not the Earth), and that the Milky Way glowed from the light of millions of stars that were so distant they could not be discerned by the naked eye. His discovery of spots on the Sun and craters on the Moon meant that these heavenly bodies were not "perfect and unblemished"—a belief that was propounded by Aristotle and insisted on by the Catholic Church. One authority, in a classic case of spin-doctoring, went so far as to declare that the Moon was encased in an invisible crystalline shield which preserved its perfectly smooth and unblemished integrity.

Gutenberg, Johannes: (1398-1468) Invented the printing press around 1450 and revolutionized the world. Before Gutenberg it would take a single monk 20 years to copy the Bible, and there were only 30,000 handwritten Bibles in the entire world. Fifty years after Gutenberg there were more than 10 million Bibles in print!

Hadley, John: (1692-1743) Everybody knows that Sir Isaac Newton invented the reflecting telescope in 1668, and the assumption is that astronomy took a giant leap forward from that point. The only problem is that Newton's telescope didn't work very well. It had a mirror that was only 1.3 inches in diameter and the image was seriously distorted by spherical aberration, i.e., not all light rays would come to focus at the same point. As a result, the telescope was not very useful. Fifty years later, the English mathematician John Hadley discovered how to make a parabolic mirror, which solved the problem of spherical aberration and opened the door to making much larger telescopes with superior images.

Hercules/Atlas: These two craters are paired because of the legend which entwined them both. Atlas was one of the Titans of Greek mythology whose punishment for siding in a war against Zeus was to hold the celestial sphere on his shoulders (some versions say it was the Earth).

To propitiate for having killed his wife and children in a fit of temporary insanity induced by Hera, Hercules was assigned 12 labors that were so difficult they seemed impossible. One of these labors was to steal three golden apples that Hera had given to Zeus as a wedding present. Hercules learned that the secret to getting the apples was to send Atlas to do the job. Atlas agreed to do so, providing Hercules took over the task of holding up the celestial sphere while he was gone. Atlas recovered the apples and fully intended to leave Hercules holding his burden forever, but Hercules tricked him into holding the sphere "just for a moment" while he got some padding for his shoulders. In what was possibly the first reported stereotype of "all brawn and no brain," Atlas agreed and Hercules fled the scene with the apples.

Hipparchus: (190-125 BCE) Greek astronomer who discovered the precession of the equinoxes and was the founder of trigonometry. He also established the magnitude system which we use today by which stars were classified by their brightness (magnitude 1 being the brightest and magnitude 6 being the dimmest). Hipparchus is also credited with having invented the astrolabe,[85] and he calculated the mean lunar month to within one second of today's accepted value!

Kepler, Johannes: (1571-1630) German astronomer, mathematician, and astrologer who made the enormously important discovery that planets move in elliptical orbits, not perfect circles. His *Three Laws of Planetary Motion* finally allowed astronomers to calculate the position of planets with much greater precision. (However, Mercury continued to avoid being pinned down. It took an Einstein to make the far-reaching discovery that planets do not precisely obey Newton's laws of gravity because gravity, as it was classically understood, did not exist. Planets are locked into their orbits, not because of gravity, but because space itself is curved!)

---

[85] The astrolabe was a medieval instrument capable of making astronomical calculations that today seem impossible without a modern computer. For an inexpensive but highly accurate modern astrolabe, go to *http://www.astrolabes.org/index.htm* and click on The Personal Astrolabe.

An interesting piece of trivia about Kepler is that personal hygiene was not high on his list of priorities. At one point, he noted in his diary that as a result of his wife's constant pesterings he finally agreed to take a bath. The result? He found the experience to be "unpleasant."

Laplace, Pierre: (1749-1827) Promontorium Laplace is named after the French astronomer and mathematician Pierre Laplace who suggested, long before their discovery, the possibility of black holes. He pointed out that some stars could be so massive that their gravitational pull could prevent even light from escaping their surface. He also proposed, 100 years before their discovery by Edwin Hubble, that there were separate galaxies beyond the Milky Way, and he independently formulated the "Nebula Hypothesis" for the origin of the solar system.

Lippershey, Hans: (1570-1619) was a Dutch spectacle maker who is generally credited with having invented the telescope in 1608. (There is an apocryphal story that a small child, playing in Lippershey's workshop, picked up two lenses, placed one before the other, was excited by what he saw and showed it to Lippershey.) Galileo got wind of the invention, made some improvements, turned it on the skies and launched the modern era of astronomy. (Although Galileo never overtly stated that he invented the telescope, he didn't exactly rush to correct others who gave him credit for the instrument.)

Messier, Charles: (1730-1817) There is virtually no other figure in the pantheon of famous scientists who is more significant to amateur astronomers than Charles Messier. Messier's most important function, as he saw it, was to hunt down comets. It was his greatest passion, but he was frequently frustrated in his efforts because he kept stumbling across faint fuzzy objects that looked like comets but proved to be nebulas or galaxies. The only way to tell the difference was to come back days later and look at it again. If it had moved, it was a comet.

So that he could avoid repeating the disappointment every time he ran across one of these items, he created a list of 110 "nuisance objects"—things to be avoided when you're hunting comets. But because these objects happen to be the most interesting things in the sky to look at, today's amateur astronomers have turned vice into virtue. Observing all 110 of the items on Messier's list is the number one goal of many fledging astronomers, and there are many who consider that you're not a "real" astronomer until you have done so.

Newton, Isaac: (1643-1727) Arguably the greatest scientist who ever lived. When Cambridge University was closed in 1665 because of the plague, Newton returned home. During this 18 month hiatus he invented calculus, discovered that white light was a composite of all colors, and, if we are to believe the legend, had a famous encounter with an apple which led to his discovery of the nature of gravity and the eventual publication of the *Principia*, the Holy Grail of the laws of physics which, among other things, allowed scientists to calculate the orbits of planets with great accuracy. Newton also revolutionized astronomy by inventing a telescope which used mirrors, instead of lenses, to gather light.

Plato: (424-348 BCE) Greek philosopher who was a student of Socrates and the teacher of Aristotle. Plato believed that the human senses could not reliably grasp reality, as exemplified most famously in his parable of the cave where a group of prisoners are chained with their backs to a cave entrance. The only thing they can see is the play of shadows thrown against the wall from outside the cave. Because they have never actually seen the real figures that are casting the shadows, they believe that the shadows themselves are the only reality. Plato believes that humanity is no better off than the prisoners: what we firmly believe to be reality has no more substance than the shadows on the walls. It would require a truly extraordinary human being to break free of the chains and make his way into the light of understanding. Alas, when such a person returns to report his findings to the others, he will be met only with disbelief and scorn.

It may be difficult for modern day thinkers to accept Plato's belief that the senses cannot be trusted—after all, seeing is believing, right? But consider this example of how easily we can be convinced that a shadow image is absolute truth.

Take a look at the photo to the right. Square B, although it is in a shadow, is obviously lighter than square A, right? Now take a 3x5 card and punch two holes in it so that one hole will fit over square A and the other over square B. Place the holes over the two squares and compare their shades. Then ask yourself if Plato was right—that, indeed, the human senses cannot reliably grasp reality.

Ptolemy, Claudius: (c. 90-160 CE) Greek astronomer and mathematician whose most important work was the *Almagest*, a treatise explaining the motions of the stars and planets. His description used a convoluted system of cycles and epicycles to explain the retrograde movement of the planets. He wrote at length about the pseudo-science of astrology and his explanation of an Earth-centered universe predominated for 1,500 years. Referring to Ptolemy, Carl Sagan once quipped, "Intellectual brilliance is no guarantee against being dead wrong."

Pythagoras: (c. 580-500 BCE) Greek philosopher whose specialty was numbers and their meanings. He gave us the Pythagorean theorem and was one of the earliest to propose that the Earth was a sphere and that the Earth, Moon, and (alas!) the stars all revolved around the Sun.

Riccioli, Giovanni Battista: (1598-1671) Italian Jesuit priest and astronomer who created a system of nomenclature for lunar features that is still in use today. Riccioli was also the first person to discover a binary star, Mizar in Ursa Major.

It is perhaps indicative of his own sense of self-importance that the crater Riccioli is larger than the magnificent craters Copernicus, Kepler, and Tycho.

When Riccioli gave the crater Copernicus its name, he actually intended it as an insult. Being a dedicated supporter of Church doctrine, Riccioli believed that Copernicus's theory that the Sun was at the center of planetary revolution was, well, revolutionary—and disruptive to Church stability. As a result, he deliberately placed Copernicus near areas of the Moon that were named after storms, tempests, and similarly unpleasant things. In Riccioli's own words, he "flung Copernicus into the Ocean of Storms." However, the idea backfired. Copernicus is one of the most fetching of all craters, and every time astronomers turn their telescopes on this feature they are paying tribute to the great man.

Seleucus: (fl. 150s BCE) Seleucus of Selucia, the man after whom the crater was named, deserves to be better known. He was a Greek philosopher and astronomer who ardently defended the heliocentric theory proposed by Aristarchus of Samos 100 years earlier. Seleucus was also the *last* heliocentric defender until Copernicus! In spite of their many significant contributions, Aristotle, Ptolemy, and their powerful earth-centered ilk managed to set back the progress of astronomy for 1,500 years. Kenneth Davis reports in his book *Don't Know Much About the Universe* that the Catholic Church did not officially concede that the Earth revolved around the Sun until 1922!

Appendix B: Pronunciation Guide

catena /kuh.TEEN.uh/ . . . . crater chain

dorsa /DOR.suh/ . . . . group of ridges

dorsum /DOR.sum/ . . . . ridge

lacus /LAH.kus/ . . . . lake

Lacus Mortis /MOR.tiss/ . . . . Lake of Death

mare /MAH.ray/ . . . . sea (pl. maria)

Mare Anguis /AHN.gwis/ . . . . Serpent Sea

Mare Crisium /CRY.see.um/ . . . . Sea of Crises

Mare Fecunditatis /fih.KUHN.di.TAH.tiss/ . . . . Sea of Fertility

Mare Frigoris /frih.GOR.iss/ . . . . Sea of Cold

Mare Humorum /hyoo.MOR.um/ . . . . Sea of Moisture

Mare Imbrium /IM.bree.uhm/ . . . . Sea of Rain

Mare Insularum /IN.suh.LAR.um/ . . . . Sea of Islands

Mare Nectaris /nek.TAR.iss/ . . . . Sea of Nectar

Mare Nubium /NOO.be.um/ . . . . Sea of Clouds

Mare Serenitatis /suh.REN.ih.TAH.tiss/ . . . . Sea of Serenity

Mare Tranquillitatis /trang.KWIL.ih.TAH.tiss/ . . . . Sea of Tranquillity

Mare Vaporum /vay.POR.uhm/ . . . . Sea of Vapors

mons /mahns/ . . . . mountain; mount

montes /MAHN.teez/ . . . . mountain range

Oceanus Procellarum /oh.SEE.uh.nuhs pro.suh.LAR.um/ . . . Ocean of Storms

palus /PAY.luhs/ . . . . marsh

Palus Epidemiarum /EH.pih.DEM.ih.AHR.um/ . . . . Marsh of Epidemics

Palus Putredinis /pyoo.TREE.din.us/ . . . . Marsh of Decay

promontorium /PRAH.muhn.TOR.ee.um/ . . . . promontory

rima /REE.muh/ . . . . rille

rimae /REE.mee/ . . . . rilles

rupes /ROO.puhz/ . . . . scarp

sinus /SIGH.nus/ . . . . bay

Sinus Asperitatis /ass.PER.ih.TAH.tiss/ . . . . Bay of Roughness

Sinus Iridum /EAR.uh.dum/ . . . . Bay of Rainbows

Sinus Medii /MEE.dee.eye/ . . . . Central Bay

Sinus Roris /ROR.is/ . . . . Bay of Dews

valis /VAH.lis/ . . . . valley

About the Author

Andrew Planck wears many hats. He has been an enthusiastic astronomer for over 50 years, is apt in foreign languages, and is an accomplished musician on the piano, autoharp, didgeridoo, musical spoons, alphorn, and Highland bagpipe. Andrew was Pipe Major of the award winning City of Denver Bagpipe Band for 12 years.

He is an active member of the Longmont Astronomical Society and is an active poster on FRAC—Front Range Astronomical Community.

Andrew is a volunteer astronomer at the Little Thompson Observatory in Berthoud, Colorado. Since its inception in 1999, over 60,000 children and adults have enjoyed presentations free of charge provided to the public and schools.

Retiring from teaching French to middle school children, he was a recipient of the Young Educator Award given by the Colorado Congress of Foreign Language Teachers. With his love of learning, he holds double B.A. degrees in French and English Literature. Using a scholarship won from the University of Colorado, Denver, he studied in France for a year.

Andrew has two married daughters, Sarah and Stefanie. Andrew is also a member of Mensa and lives with his wife, Susan, in Boulder, Colorado. *What's Hot on the Moon Tonight* is his first book.

Schedule an astronomy presentation for your Group, School and *Create a Lunar Experience*—he brings the telescopes, you supply the group!

Contact Andrew through his website at: *AndrewPlanck.com*

Or via email: APlanck@comcast.net

Index

(Main entries are indicated by bold type.)

[Created with **TExtract** / *www.Texyz.com*]

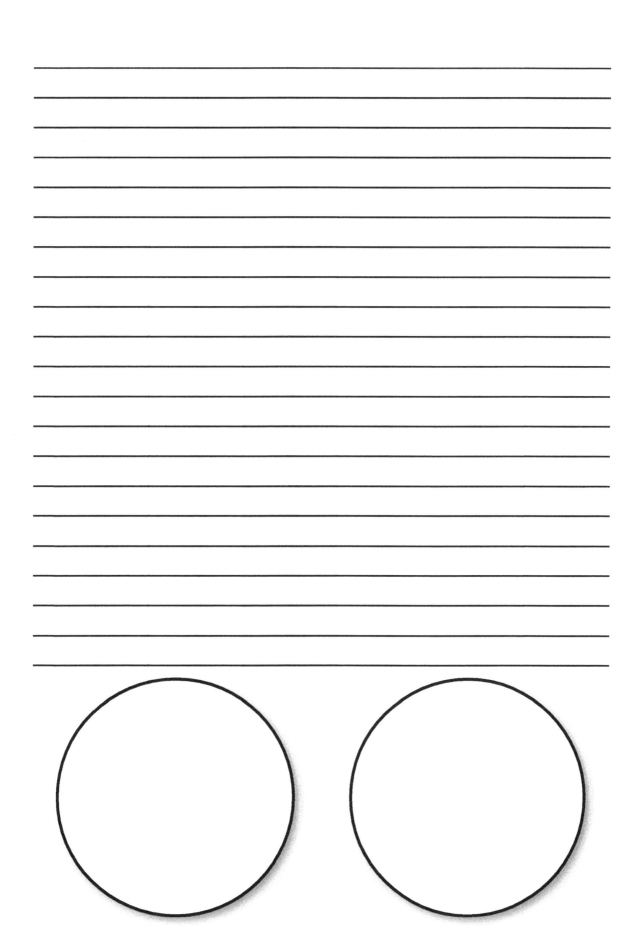

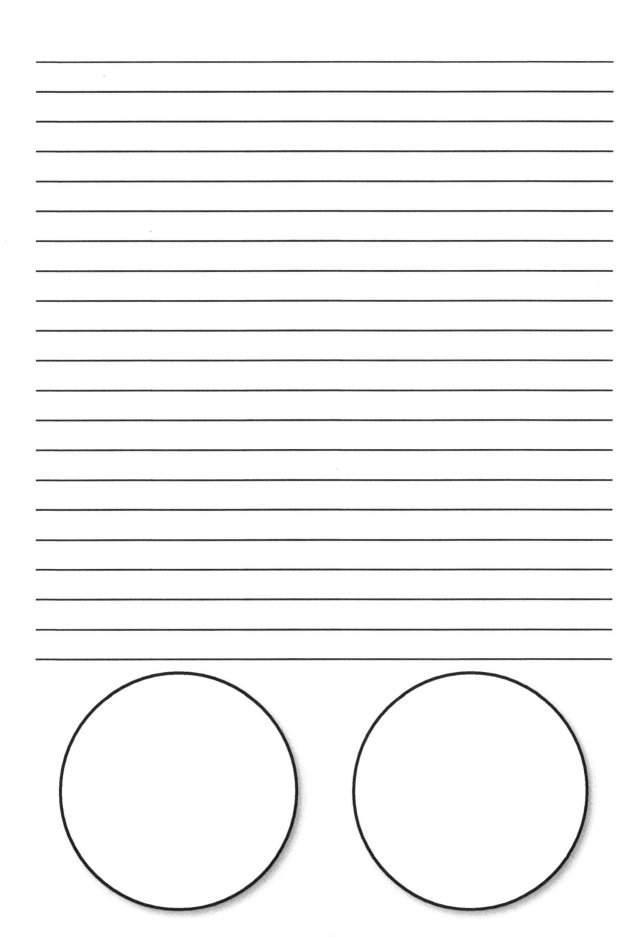

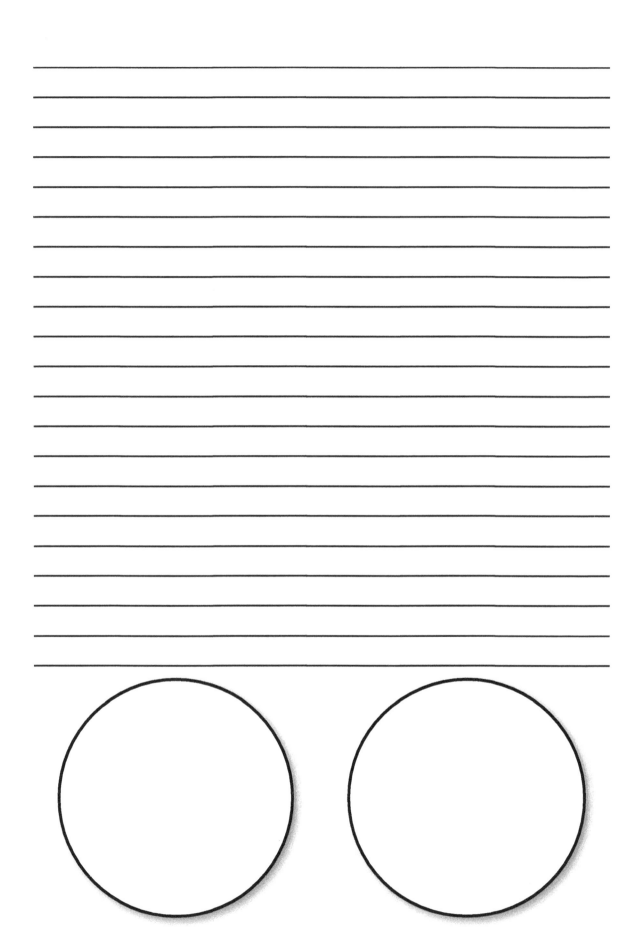

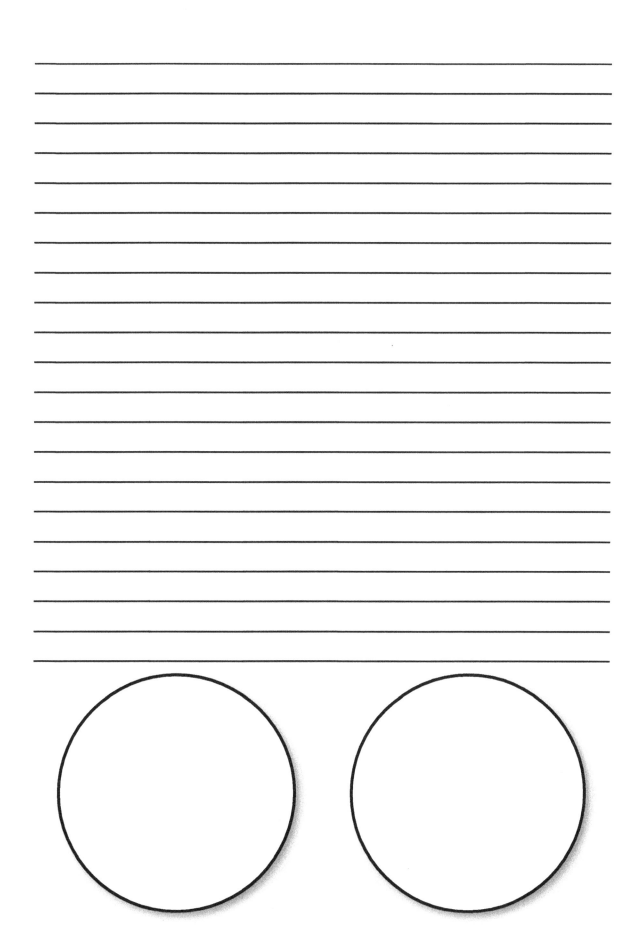

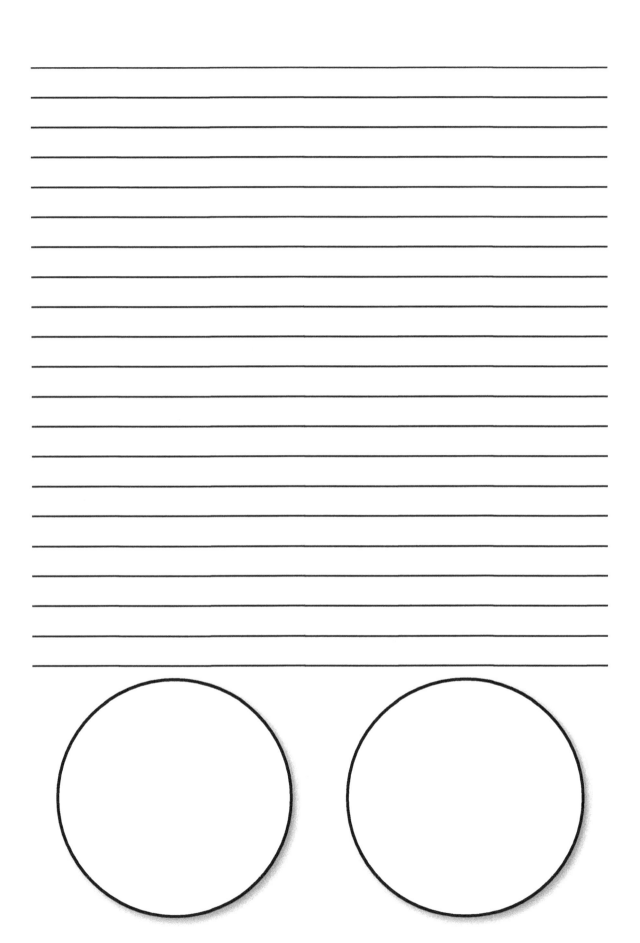

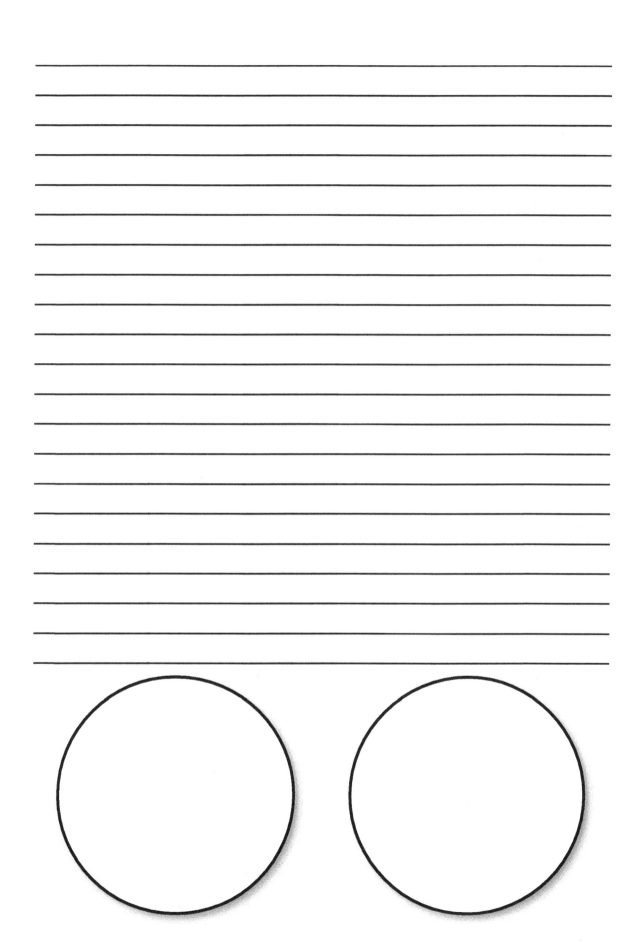

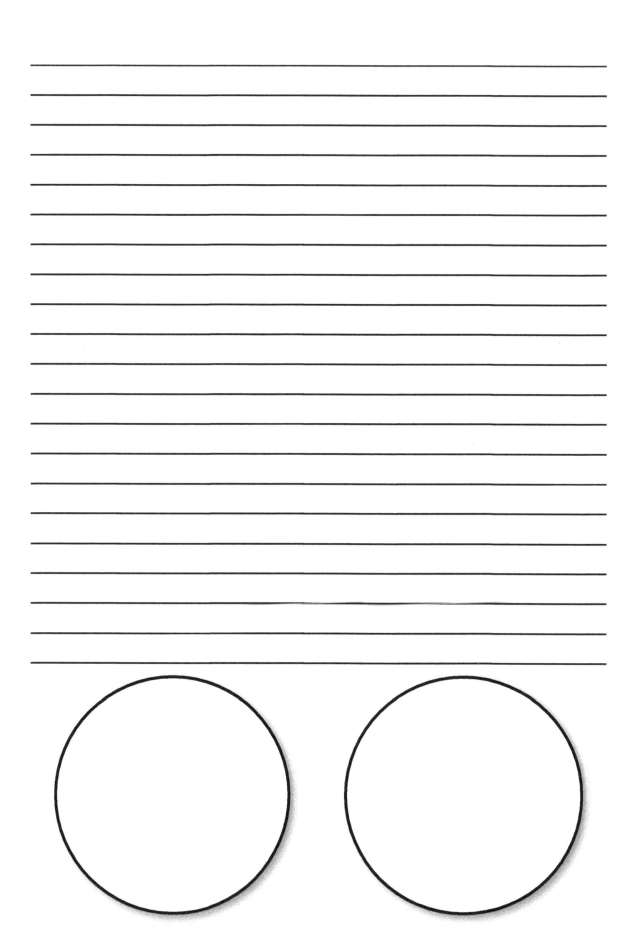

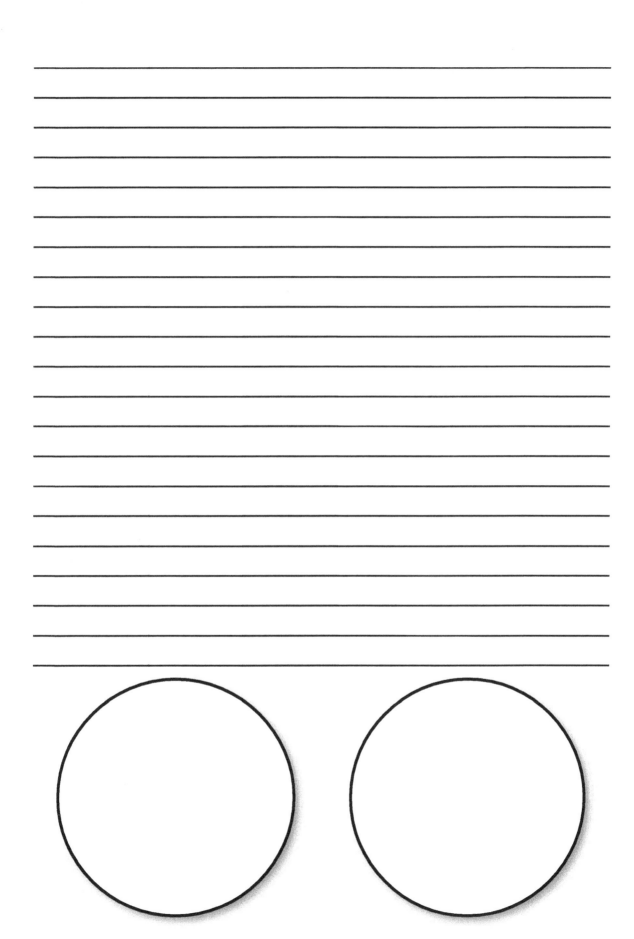

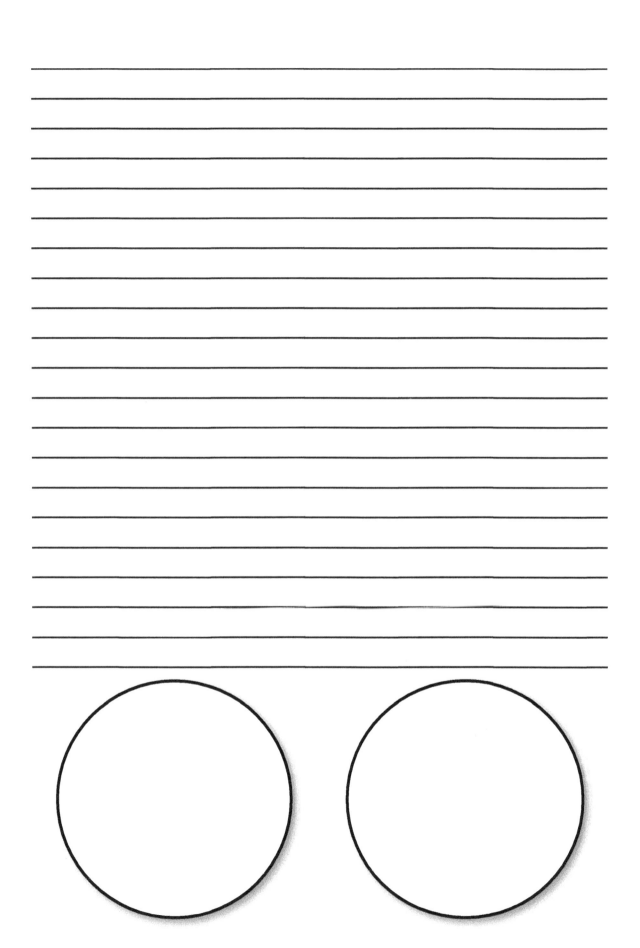

Date: _____ Lunar Day: _____   Date: _____ Lunar Day: _____

Name: _____ From p. #: _____   Name: _____ From p. #: _____

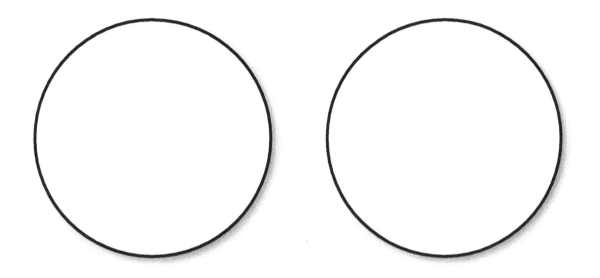

Date: _____ Lunar Day: _____   Date: _____ Lunar Day: _____

Name: _____ From p. #: _____   Name: _____ From p. #: _____

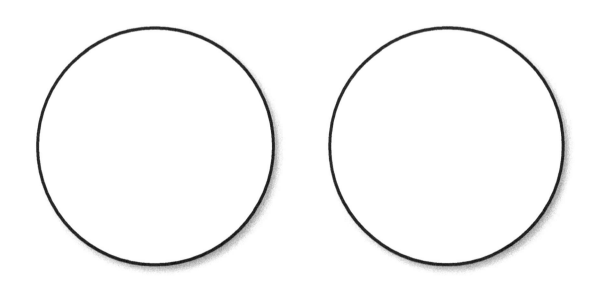

Date: _____ Lunar Day: _____ Date: _____ Lunar Day: _____

Name: _____ From p. #: _____ Name: _____ From p. #: _____

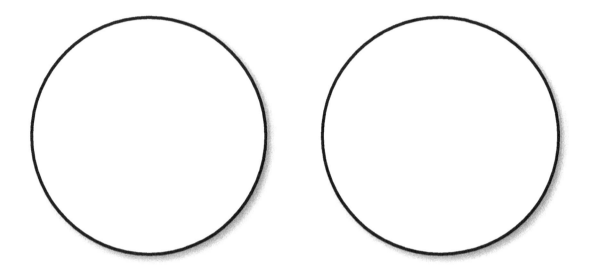

Date: _____ Lunar Day: _____ Date: _____ Lunar Day: _____

Name: _____ From p. #: _____ Name: _____ From p. #: _____

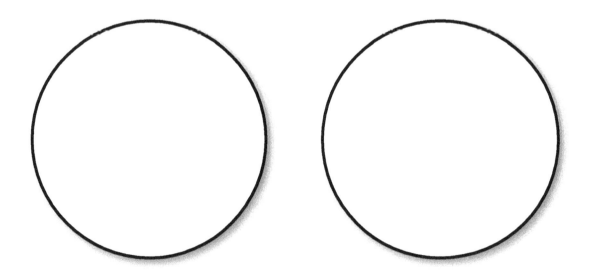

Date: _____ Lunar Day: _____   Date: _____ Lunar Day: _____

Name: _____ From p. #: _____   Name: _____ From p. #: _____

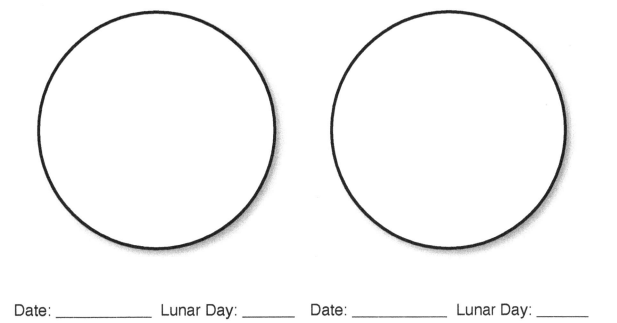

Date: _____ Lunar Day: _____   Date: _____ Lunar Day: _____

Name: _____ From p. #: _____   Name: _____ From p. #: _____

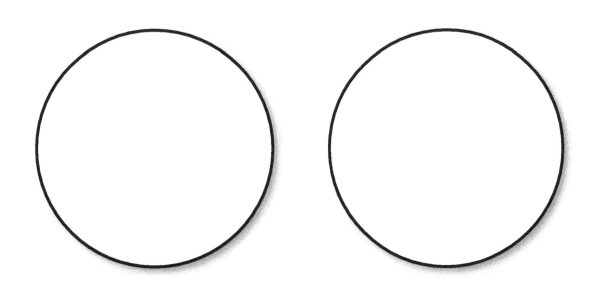

Date: _____ Lunar Day: _____   Date: _____ Lunar Day: _____

Name: _____ From p. #: _____   Name: _____ From p. #: _____

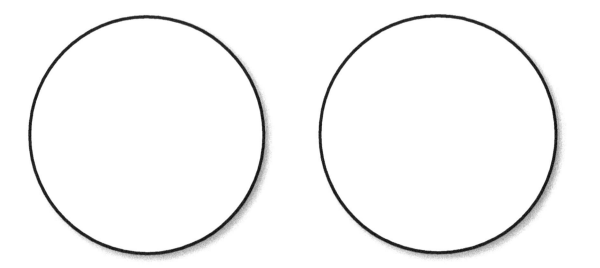

Date: _____ Lunar Day: _____   Date: _____ Lunar Day: _____

Name: _____ From p. #: _____   Name: _____ From p. #: _____

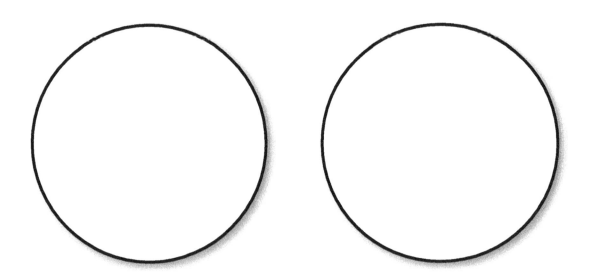

Date: _____ Lunar Day: _____   Date: _____ Lunar Day: _____

Name: _____ From p. #: _____   Name: _____ From p. #: _____

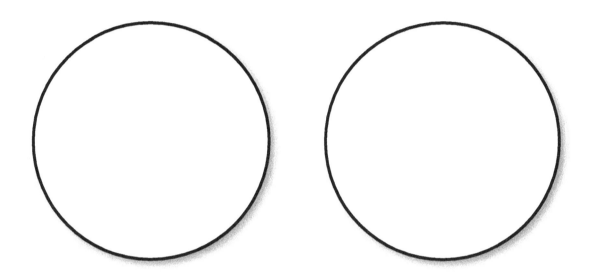

Date: _____ Lunar Day: _____   Date: _____ Lunar Day: _____

Name: _____ From p. #: _____   Name: _____ From p. #: _____

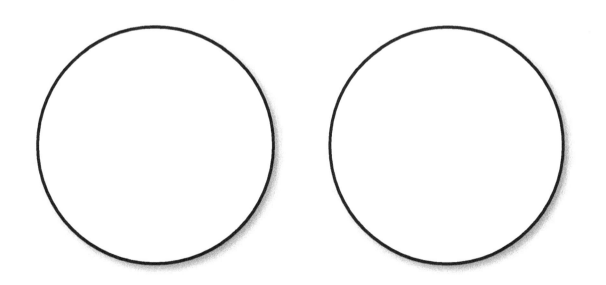

Date: _____ Lunar Day: _____   Date: _____ Lunar Day: _____

Name: _____ From p. #: _____   Name: _____ From p. #: _____

Date: _____ Lunar Day: _____   Date: _____ Lunar Day: _____

Name: _____ From p. #: _____   Name: _____ From p. #: _____

Date: _____ Lunar Day: _____   Date: _____ Lunar Day: _____

Name: _____ From p. #: _____   Name: _____ From p. #: _____

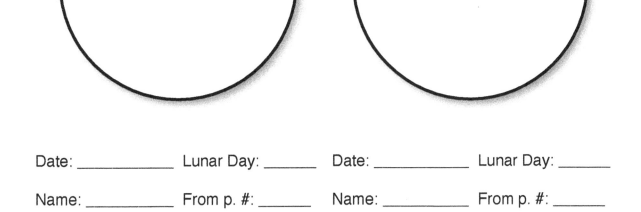

Date: _____ Lunar Day: _____   Date: _____ Lunar Day: _____

Name: _____ From p. #: _____   Name: _____ From p. #: _____

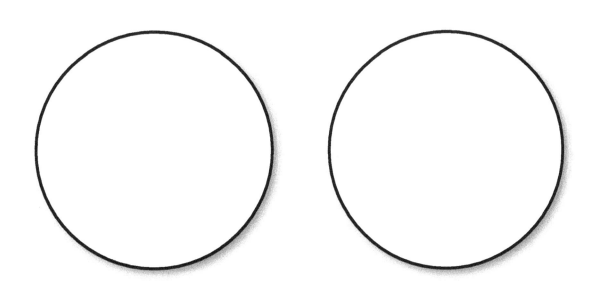

Date: _____ Lunar Day: _____ Date: _____ Lunar Day: _____

Name: _____ From p. #: _____ Name: _____ From p. #: _____

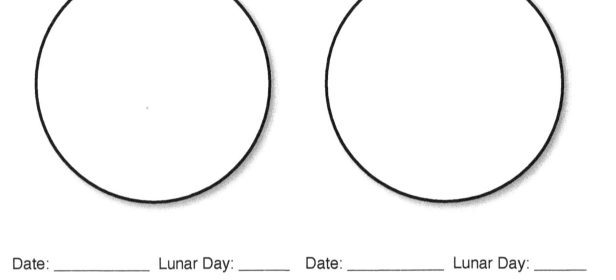

Date: _____ Lunar Day: _____ Date: _____ Lunar Day: _____

Name: _____ From p. #: _____ Name: _____ From p. #: _____

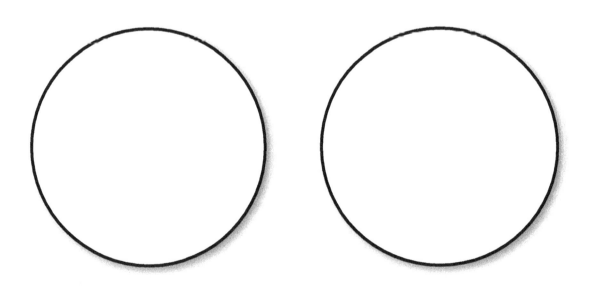

Date: _____ Lunar Day: _____   Date: _____ Lunar Day: _____

Name: _____ From p. #: _____   Name: _____ From p. #: _____

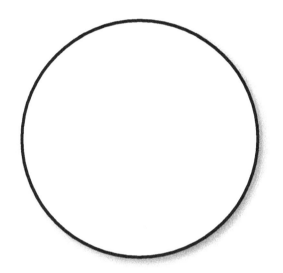
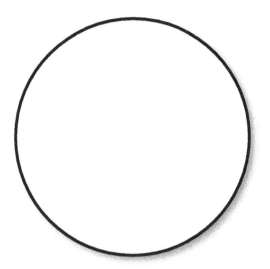

Date: _____ Lunar Day: _____   Date: _____ Lunar Day: _____

Name: _____ From p. #: _____   Name: _____ From p. #: _____

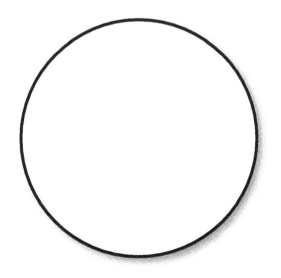
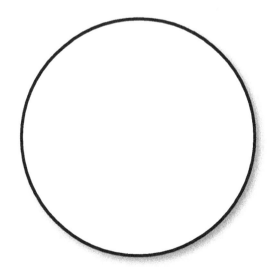

Date: _____ Lunar Day: _____ Date: _____ Lunar Day: _____

Name: _____ From p. #: _____ Name: _____ From p. #: _____

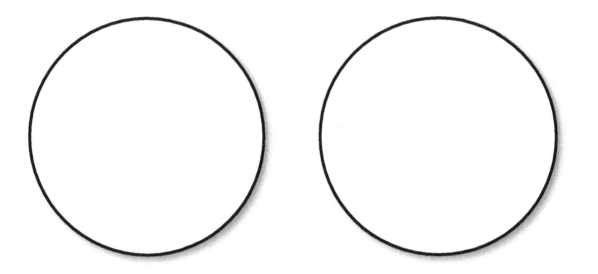

Date: _____ Lunar Day: _____ Date: _____ Lunar Day: _____

Name: _____ From p. #: _____ Name: _____ From p. #: _____

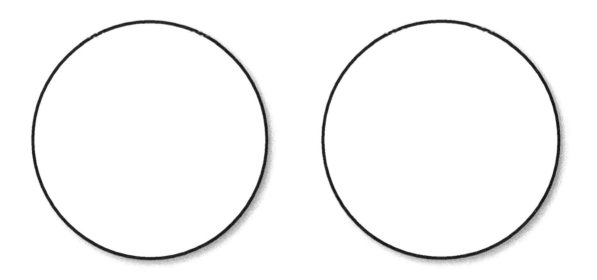

Date: _____ Lunar Day: _____   Date: _____ Lunar Day: _____

Name: _____ From p. #: _____   Name: _____ From p. #: _____

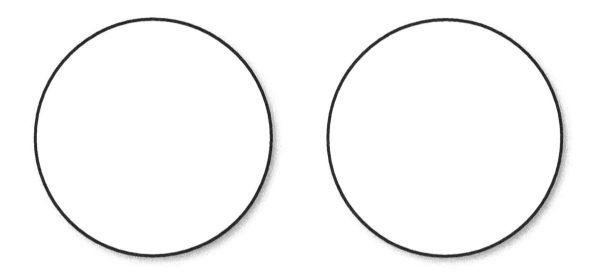

Date: _____ Lunar Day: _____   Date: _____ Lunar Day: _____

Name: _____ From p. #: _____   Name: _____ From p. #: _____

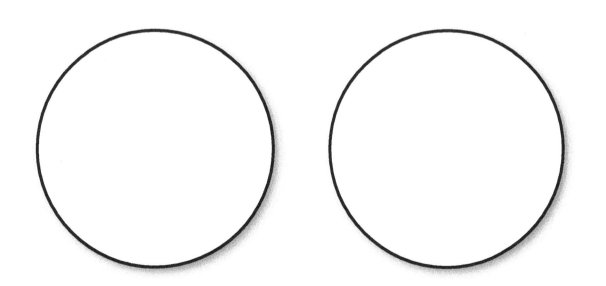

Date: _____ Lunar Day: _____ Date: _____ Lunar Day: _____

Name: _____ From p. #: _____ Name: _____ From p. #: _____

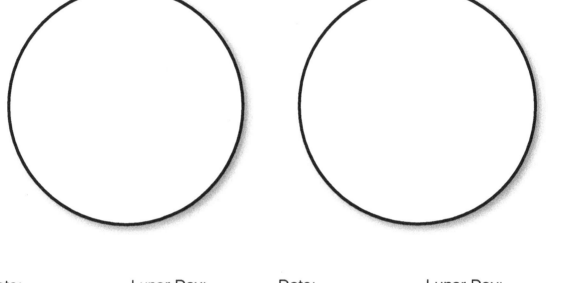

Date: _____ Lunar Day: _____ Date: _____ Lunar Day: _____

Name: _____ From p. #: _____ Name: _____ From p. #: _____

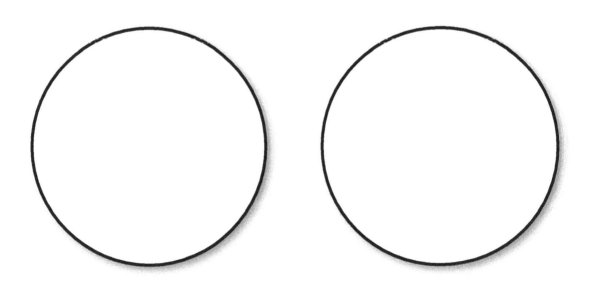

Date: _____ Lunar Day: _____   Date: _____ Lunar Day: _____

Name: _____ From p. #: _____   Name: _____ From p. #: _____

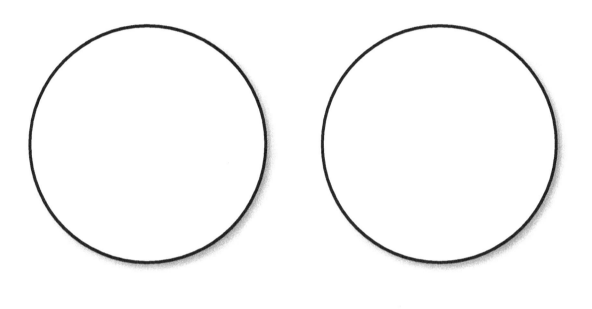

Date: _____ Lunar Day: _____   Date: _____ Lunar Day: _____

Name: _____ From p. #: _____   Name: _____ From p. #: _____

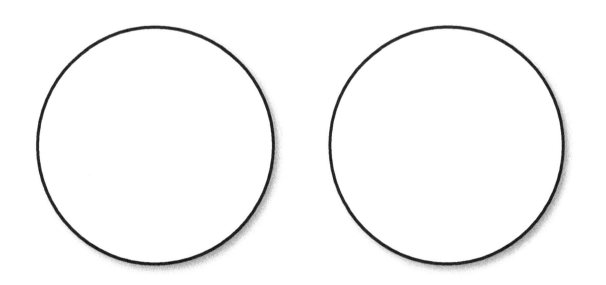

Date: _____ Lunar Day: _____   Date: _____ Lunar Day: _____

Name: _____ From p. #: _____   Name: _____ From p. #: _____

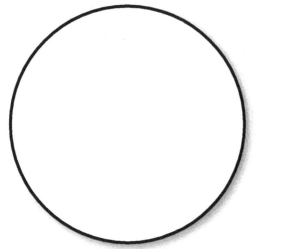

Date: _____ Lunar Day: _____   Date: _____ Lunar Day: _____

Name: _____ From p. #: _____   Name: _____ From p. #: _____

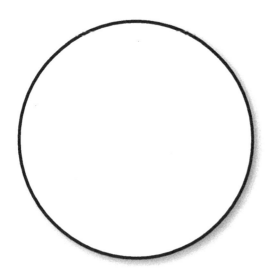

TPS 143117